A

D1047085

The Man
Who Ruined
Football

Books by Elston Brooks

THE MAN WHO RUINED FOOTBALL
COLUMN, WRITE!
WITH A CAST OF THOUSANDS
I'VE HEARD THOSE SONGS BEFORE
DON'T DRY-CLEAN MY BLACKJACK

The Man Who Ruined Football

A NOVEL BY

Elston Brooks

Pasco County Library System
Overdue notices are a courtesy of the Library System.
Failure to receive an overdue notice does not absolve the borrower of the obligation to return the materials on time.

Atheneum

NEW YORK • 1989

HUDSON BRANCH LIBRARY

For my wife, Pam Brooks,
and my friend, Pat Biggers

This is a work of fiction and the story and events it
tells are entirely fictional. Certain real persons, teams,
games and places are mentioned in the book for purposes of
enhancing and adding reality to the story. Obviously, the
fictionalized events involving real persons, teams, games
and places did not occur.

Copyright © 1989 by Elston Brooks

All rights reserved. No part of this book may be reproduced or transmitted
in any form or by any means, electronic or mechanical, including photocopying,
recording or by any information storage and retrieval system, without permission in
writing from the Publisher.

Atheneum
Macmillan Pubishing Company
866 Third Avenue, New York, N.Y. 10022
Collier Macmillan Canada, Inc.

Library of Congress Cataloging-in-Publication Data
Brooks, Elston.
    The man who ruined football : a novel / by Elston Brooks.
        p.   cm.
    ISBN 0-689-12071-0
    I. Title.
PS3552.R6589M36   1989
813'.54—dc20   89-6706   CIP

10 9 8 7 6 5 4 3 2 1

Printed in the United States of America

Author's Note

This is a work of fiction. It never happened.

Therefore, the real-life characters in this novel—such as Tom Landry, Tex Schramm, Gil Brandt, Clint Murchison, Pat Summerall, John Madden, Frank Gifford, Don Meredith, Howard Cosell, Pete Rozelle, Dan Jenkins, Johnny Carson, Rafael Septien, John Dutton, Paul Harvey, Liz Smith, Don Shula, Blackie Sherrod, and others—never said the words I have put in their mouths.

My first inclination was to invent an entire mythical pro football team in place of the Dallas Cowboys, but that would have required mythical coaches and players, mythical opponents, and perhaps even a mythical counterpart to the National Football League.

Instead, I have placed the setting in 1982, which was the strike-shortened NFL season in which the teams played only half of the schedule.

There is no strike in this novel, so obviously most of the games involved weren't even played.

—ELSTON BROOKS

The Man
Who Ruined
Football

CHAPTER

·····························

1

Standing outside of the Dallas Cowboys' high-rise headquarters off North Central Expressway on a copper-hot
July afternoon in 1982, his three-piece suit not quite
holding in his slight paunch, and his attaché case looking
like a permanent appendage to his right hand, Victor F.
Waller gave the immediate appearance of a middle-aged
WASP insurance man.

All three of which he was.

With his mod spectacles and stylishly long hair, which
had turned only half gray, he could have been anywhere
from forty to fifty. But definitely middle-aged. And definitely an insurance man, even if one weren't close enough
to read his agency's name on the attaché case.

Vic Waller owned his own agency in Fort Worth and,
like most Fort Worth people, hated driving in Dallas. He
had taken two wrong turns after leaving I-30, which he
still referred to as the Dallas turnpike even though the
tolls had been lifted from the old toll road for five years
now. Even so, he was ten minutes early for his appointment with Cowboy coach Tom Landry. Vic Waller always
allowed for wrong turns in Dallas.

He also allowed time for a last cigarette outside the
entrance of the Cowboy headquarters. Waller was a two-
pack-a-day man, and while he had never met Tom Landry,

he felt he knew, without really knowing, that there would
be no ashtray on Landry's desk.

Waller mused to himself that he never dreamed he'd
ever be seeing the Cowboy headquarters, much less having an appointment with Tom Landry. And he certainly
never dreamed how easy the appointment had been to
arrange. He had always assumed a one-on-one with Landry
was one of those things forever denied to a member of the
general public. Perhaps it was like the glamorous movie
star who sat at home every night because no men thought
they could call her for a date.

Of course Waller knew he wasn't getting in to see Tom
Landry to sell him insurance. Waller knew he had information that Tom Landry would like to know.

Two days ago Vic had walked into his office in a
downtown Fort Worth skyscraper and asked his secretary
to get Dan Jenkins on the line at his *Sports Illustrated*
office in New York.

To Vic's surprise, Jenkins was not only in his office,
but answered his own phone.

"Mr. Jenkins," Waller began, "you don't know me, but
I'm calling from Fort Worth, which I understand is your
hometown. I'm afraid I'm just a fan of yours who decided
this morning that I was long overdue in telling you of my
admiration."

"I like the conversation so far," Jenkins replied.

"I've followed your career ever since you and Blackie
Sherrod and Bud Shrake were all at the *Press* here. You
guys were the greatest. And then I followed all of you
when you went over to Dallas. And I never miss your stuff
in *Sports Illustrated*."

"You've got great credentials," Jenkins said. "Thanks."

"But what I really admire is your books," Vic continued. "I think *Semi-Tough* is the funniest book I
ever read. But permit me to say that I was buying your
books long before *Semi-Tough*. I've read *Saturday's*

America twice and *The Dogged Victims of Inexorable Fate* three times."

"That's more than my wife has read them," Dan laughed. "I can see that you're a person of perception and deep insight." Jenkins silently cussed himself. He was beginning to lap up this long-distance adulation from a stranger.

"I'll tell you what a great writer you are," Vic said. "I don't play golf, I don't like golf, I don't watch golf on TV. Yet, you can make me read a golf story just by the way you write it."

"Well, that's very nice of you to say so," Jenkins responded.

"I hope you don't mind my telephonic intrusion this morning," Vic said. "But I just got down to my office and said to myself, 'Why don't I phone him and tell him how much pleasure he brings to people?' So I did."

"Of course I don't mind! I'm human too. We all like a pat on the head sometimes." Jenkins gave a little chuckle. Christ, he thought to himself, the guy even has me giving phony chuckles.

Vic took a deep breath and said, "There *is* one thing I'd like to ask you, though. It's been nagging me for years, but I never realized I'd have the chance to ask you until now. Now that I have you on the phone, I wonder if you could clear it up for me?"

"Why certainly. What is it?"

"Were you the one who shit in Clarence Buford's sun helmet that day in 1943 up at the school?"

Jenkins let it soak in for a second and then exploded in laughter. "That's beautiful," he said. "Who the fuck is this?"

"You better hope it ain't Clarence Buford. He grew up to be tougher than hammered apeshit," Vic said.

"Vic!" Dan exclaimed.

"Jenkie," Vic said in answer.

"Vic, you asshole, I haven't seen you in so many years I didn't recognize your voice. The last time June and I came down for the Colonial, Jerre Todd said you were a recluse who didn't come out of the house anymore."

"Oh, I come out and play occasionally."

"I hope you're still boxin' that old fur around."

"I quit. They're all too young. The last one I dated said she never knew Dean Martin and Jerry Lewis used to be partners."

"Girl at a party up here the other night asked me who was that President we had who was in a wheelchair," Jenkins said glumly.

"Jenkie, I need a favor. I know you know Tom Landry, and I was wondering if you could get me in to see him."

"Sure. I mean I could call him to get you an appointment. But you could do that yourself. He's really a friendly guy."

"All I need you to do," Vic said, "is to vouch for me with Landry that I'm not a nut or just a fan who wants to meet him. I have some information for him that I know he'd want to have."

"Can I tell him what it's about?" Dan asked. "It might help."

"It's about a player . . . a kicker," Waller said. "But, see, that's where I need you to vouch for me as a non-nut. There must be thousands of guys wanting to tout players to Landry."

"Well, at least hundreds," Jenkins said. "I'll see what I can do."

Jenkins called Vic back within an hour. "You're on," he said. "Wednesday at three P.M. in Landry's office."

"I may go over on Tuesday and wait," Waller said.

"One other thing," Dan said. "Can your kicker speak English?"

"Yes."

"That's refreshing. They're all a bunch of crazy fuckers."

4

Now, at exactly 2:58—and Waller knew it was exactly 2:58 because he wore an Accutron—Waller flipped away his Kent and entered the building to take the elevator to the eleventh floor.

A receptionist directed him down the hall to the office of Landry's secretary, Barbara Goodman. Yes, she said, he was expected and would he come this way, please. She ushered him into Landry's spacious corner office and said, "This is Mr. Waller from Fort Worth."

"Victor Waller," Vic said, extending his hand as Landry rose and walked from behind his desk to shake hands.

"I'm glad to meet you, Mr. Waller," Landry said, smiling. "Dan Jenkins says you two have been friends since grade school. Have a seat."

Waller couldn't get over that smile. Tom Landry seemed to be smiling with every word he spoke. There was no trace of the stone-face image that Landry presented on TV. Waller realized that it was true, as Landry had explained in interviews over the years, that in those sideline shots he was concentrating on the next play, too involved to be smiling over the success of a current play.

Landry resettled himself behind his desk, a desk as neat as the man himself. Even in the privacy of his own office during the off-season, Landry was wearing a coat and tie. And the desk wasn't wearing an ashtray, Vic noted, although there was one in the outer office for visitors. Vic never even considered using it.

"Coach Landry," Vic began, "I promised myself I wouldn't say I was the Cowboys' biggest fan, and your greatest admirer, because I know everyone says that. But I'm going to say it anyway."

"Well, I certainly appreciate that, Mr. Waller. We don't get tired of hearing it."

Waller liked the fact that Landry said "we."

"What I really wanted to say first, I'll say now," Vic continued. "I am aware of the demands on your time, and

I appreciate very much you giving me this appointment, especially since it's about a player. I know how many people must be bothering you about getting tryouts for the Dallas Cowboys."

"I'm always interested in football players." Landry smiled. "Believe it or not, Gil Brandt misses some. I guess you know how many starters we've gotten over the years who were walk-ons."

"Good. I think you'll want this one."

"Dan said he was a kicker."

"Yes."

"Are you his agent?"

"No . . . not at all. I'm just here to tell you about him."

"Well, I'm ready to listen. We happen to have the best in the NFL right now with Rafael Septien, but just the other day Gil and I drove ninety miles to look at one. As I said, I'm always interested in football players."

"I also remember the year the Cowboys conducted that Kick Karavan, I think you called it, going all over the nation to audition kickers," Vic put in. Immediately he wished he hadn't used the word "audition." Too late, though.

"We got Mac Percival out of that," Landry said. "And one year Gil went all the way to Austria to recruit Toni Fritsch."

"Your first soccer-style kicker," Vic said.

"Is your man a soccer-style kicker?" Landry asked.

"No. Straightaway."

"Not many of them around today," Landry said. "Tell me about him."

And so, here it was. The Big Revelation. Vic took a deep breath and leaned forward in his chair. As he did his foot nudged his attaché case, causing it to topple over. He leaned down to right it, wishing he had a cigarette.

"Coach Landry," Vic began, "what would you say if I told you he was a can't-miss kicker?"

Tom Landry was too polite to say there is no such thing. Instead, he said, "I'd say I'd want to take a look at him. What's his range?"

Waller sighed. "Coach, this is where it gets sticky. This is where I don't want you to think I'm a nut . . ."

Landry waited.

Waller frowned as he said, "I could tell you he can make it from any part of the field. But the fact is, he can make it the length of the field. He can kick from under one goalpost and put it through the other goalpost."

Landry didn't say anything.

"Of course," Vic said lamely, "I realize no one would ever be kicking from under a goalpost because that would be putting the kicker standing out of the end zone, but let's say from the one-yard line . . ."

Damn! Vic said to himself. *Why am I stupidly sitting here telling Tom Landry the rules of football!*

Landry waved his hand at that and smiled. "You're saying he can make 109-yard field goals?"

"Yes."

"Consistently?"

"Yes."

Landry leaned back in his chair. "Do you realize what all that means? What the results of that would mean?"

"Yes, sir, perhaps even better than you do at this particular moment. Because you're hearing about it for the first time. I've been thinking about it a lot . . . considering all situations."

"Like . . . ?"

"Well, obviously he'd be your kickoff man. Every kickoff would go out of the end zone. You'd never have the threat of a runback. Your opponent would always be starting from the twenty."

Landry nodded.

Waller went on. "If the opponent doesn't make an eighty-yard scoring drive, they'd punt to the Cowboys. If the Cowboys didn't make a first down, they wouldn't punt on fourth down, they could kick a field goal—from any place on the field. Automatic three points and then they'd kick off again to the opponents, who, again, would have to start from the twenty."

"And it just keeps going on," Landry said.

"Exactly. Sometimes, naturally, the Cowboys would score touchdowns. But when they didn't? How many possessions does a team get in a game? Fourteen? Sixteen? That's forty-two or forty-eight points a game, if the Cowboys never scored a touchdown—and you know that's not going to happen, the Cowboys never scoring a touchdown."

Landry said, "It's not likely that a team would get that many possessions. The average per team would be lower." Landry paused, and then, as if to make Vic feel more at ease, the coach added, "Barring excessive turnovers, of course."

Damn! Vic thought again. *I didn't do my homework!* He felt in his coat pocket for the pack of Kents, but immediately removed his hand.

"I don't know where I got that possession number," he said, "but let's say ten possessions. That's thirty points—without any touchdowns."

Landry nodded, and Vic felt confident again. He plunged on.

"The only way the Cowboys could lose a game," he said, "is for the opponents to score a touchdown or a field goal on every one of their possessions, and you know that's not going to happen, either."

Landry let it all sink in. He was looking for flaws.

"The kicker has to go down under kickoffs," the coach said. "He'd be a marked man after one game. They'd go for him. Kill him. Put him out for good."

"I thought of that too," Vic said almost apologetically. "But he wouldn't *have* to go down under kickoffs. If every kick were known to go out of the end zone, *nobody* would really have to go down under kickoffs." He paused and then added, "Of course the rest of the team would go down . . ."

"You *have* thought it all out, haven't you?"

"Yes, sir, and there's one other thing I thought of. I know you don't like Danny White being both the quarterback and the punter. You're afraid he'll get hurt punting and you'll lose your quarterback."

Landry introduced the first of his familiar "No, not really" answers into his conversation with Vic. "No, not really. The main reason is that having to punt disrupts his concentration as a quarterback." But Landry saw what Victor Waller was driving at.

"With my man, you'd never be punting. You'd be going for the field goal on fourth down. You'd even be saving a spot on the roster if you were thinking about getting a new punter this year."

Landry got out of his chair and walked to the windows behind him. Looking down from the eleventh floor, he could see University Park's residential area and the SMU campus spreading off to the horizon. From the other corner window he could look down at the busy traffic speeding along North Central Expressway. He had come to love the twin views over the years and wondered idly what his view would be when the Cowboys finally moved into their new Valley Ranch complex in Dallas, which was still on the drawing boards.

Vic sat in his chair seeing the standing Landry from the back for the first time. He was impressed by the size of the man, another deception from Landry's TV sideline appearance. He was a big man, muscular, tall, wide of shoulders. Vic knew Landry had been in the backfield with both the Texas Longhorns and the New York Giants, but, football fan though he was, Vic really couldn't recall ever having seen Landry play. In fact, Vic had never heard of Tom Landry until 1960, when Landry left the Giants as an assistant coach and signed on as the first coach of the fledgling Dallas Cowboys. If he hadn't long since lost his hair, Tom Landry would have never looked his fifty-seven years of age.

Landry turned to Vic and said, "I assume your man is a free agent. We'd have heard about him in college if he played. Does he go, or did he go, to college?"

"No. He played at Paschal High in Fort Worth and lives there now. But he never got to college."

"Ah, a graduate of Nonee."

"Beg pardon?"

"Nonee College," Landry said. "That's what we call it on the roster where it gives a player's weight, height, number, position, age, NFL experience, and college. If a player didn't go to college, it says 'None.' We call it Nonee College."

Vic exclaimed, "I heard Jack Buck say that on TV one time when he was doing the play-by-play of some game. The other announcer in the booth corrected him by saying, 'That's none.' I always thought Buck had made a goof."

Tom Landry declined to sit back down. He was having his first pangs of apprehension. If this incredible find of Victor Waller's was for real, if such a superhuman kicker did exist, would he be available under the NFL rules?

"The NFL rules state the player's class must have graduated before he can be signed," Landry said to Vic. "When did his class graduate?"

"Well, let's see," Vic computed mentally. "He got out of Paschal in '47, so if he'd gone to college, his class would have been '51. Yes, '51."

Landry slowly went back and sat behind his desk.

"Are you saying," he asked Vic, "that he was class of 1951?"

"Yes. Would have been, that is, if he had attended."

"That's more than thirty years ago," Landry said. "He'd have to be over fifty now."

"He's fifty-two," Vic said.

"How old are you?" Landry asked, beginning to realize a little.

"I'm fifty-two," Vic said.

"And what's your man's name? What's the name of your kicker?"

"Victor Waller," Vic said. "I'm the kicker."

CHAPTER

....

2

Victor Waller didn't feel inclined to tell Tom Landry that until just four nights ago he hadn't kicked a football since his high school days.

Or that while it was true he had graduated from Paschal in 1947, he hadn't played since his sophomore year in 1944—thirty-eight years ago.

Or that he had never kicked on artificial turf, or on ice, or snow, or into swirling winds. Or had never kicked a field goal that was snapped and held, instead of sitting there patiently on a tee.

Or for that matter—*Oh, Christ!*—against a charging line dedicated to blocking the kick.

It had all started on a whim. An idle wondering if he could do it again. He had gone to a sporting-goods store and bought a football, a kicking tee, and some kicking shoes. Then, when night fell, he drove to the deserted football practice field of a high school near his West Side apartment. There, with the goalposts looming white in the light of a full moon, he kicked seven field goals from one end of the field to the other. Always having to trot more than a hundred yards to retrieve the ball and kick it back in the opposite direction. Always feeling that stab of pain running up the back of his fifty-two-year-old right leg.

And always without a miss.

Even if Vic had felt inclined to tell Tom Landry these things, it was too late now. Landry was on the phone calling the nearby office of Gil Brandt. With disbelieving ears, Vic was hearing Landry ask if Brandt could accompany him to the practice field to take a look at a kicker.

"Let's take two cars," Landry was saying. "I won't be coming back here. Meet you right now at the elevator."

Landry smiled at Vic as he hung up and got his hat. "Gil said he could go with us," Landry said. "We'll get you some equipment over at the field."

Vic swallowed. "I never dreamed you'd give me a tryout today," he said, "but I still brought along my shoes and shorts." He pointed to his attaché case.

"No sense in you having to come back another day," Landry said, motioning for Vic to go ahead of him back down the hall.

Gil Brandt came out of his office to join them on the way to the elevator. Landry made the introductions.

Brandt was immediately recognizable to Vic from the many pictures of him that he'd seen. He was one-fourth of the most successful management quartet in NFL history.

All four had been present from the beginning, back in 1960. Clint Murchison, Jr., the crew-cut Dallas millionaire who owned the Cowboys, was considered to be the ideal owner, a private and almost reclusive man whose only "interference" with the team was giving coach Tom Landry multiyear contracts during the team's losing years. Murchison left the running of the team to Landry and the running of the organization to president and general manager Tex Schramm. Rounding out the foursome was Brandt, the former baby-photographer whose genius at computerized scouting and finding top-quality players other teams had overlooked was legend in the NFL.

"Are you the agent?" Brandt asked Vic by way of conversation as they waited for the elevator.

Landry grinned and answered for Vic: "You're not the first one to make that mistake, Gil. Mr. Waller is the kicker."

Brandt tried not to look surprised. Vic laughed, a little weakly, and said, "You might get better used to the idea if you called me Vic. Mr. Waller was my father, and he's dead."

Seeing old guys reliving their football pasts, thinking they could still kick, if not play, with the youthful pro giants of today, was nothing new to Gil Brandt. He saw them every year when the Cowboys held their annual open tryouts. And some actually could kick. But not good enough. Not good enough to last. None ever got invited to training camp at Thousand Oaks, California, much less ever made the team. And this man hadn't even showed up when this year's tryouts were announced.

Brandt also knew that Tom Landry knew all of this. He wondered why Tom would be giving Waller a personal look on this day. Tom had to know something that he hadn't yet told Brandt.

As they rode down on the elevator, Vic said, "Until you said to take two cars, I always thought the practice field was out back of the building."

"No," said Landry, "it's about a twelve-minute drive, over on Forest Lane."

"Someday, when we finally get into our new Valley Ranch complex," Brandt said, "we'll have everything in one place."

When they got to the cars Landry indicated that Vic was to ride with him. Obviously Vic would be coming back with Brandt.

Landry drove smoothly and steadily, his eyes always straight ahead as he talked. Vic was grateful that Landry kept up the conversation during the drive after Vic asked him an opening question about the Cowboys' "chances" for the coming season.

When one asked the "chances" of America's Team one was talking about only one thing. Not wins and losses, not the playoffs, not the NFC title. Just the Super Bowl.

Vic watched the fedoraed Landry profile as the celebrated coach said the Super Bowl was the only goal. It always was with the Cowboys, he said. He spoke fondly of Vince Lombardi. "Vince used to say that winning was the only thing. I like to win, all right, but I say going to the Super Bowl is the only thing."

Tom Landry, the only coach to go to five Super Bowls, winning two, felt he should have gone to two more. Not the first two. Green Bay had proved their right to win the two championship games over the Cowboys. It was the last two Landry was talking about.

He spoke frankly of his disappointment the past two years, losing in the two championship games. The Eagles, like the two Green Bay teams of so many years ago, had proved their right to win that bitter cold Sunday in Philadelphia, but the Cowboys had come so *far* that season! And then, this past season, in San Francisco. The game all but won with fifty-one seconds to go. The Catch. Dwight Clark coming down with it in the back of the end zone.

Vic said, "He was throwing it away."

Landry looked over at him with new respect. "How so?"

"Montana had been chased all the way to the right. Too Tall Jones was jumping right in his face. Jones's hands must have been ten feet in the air. Montana was just trying to get rid of it, out of the end zone, to stop the clock. Clark wasn't the intended receiver. He just jumped up and came down with it."

"You're absolutely right," Landry said, "although I never said it at the time. It would have sounded like sour grapes, but I knew it was just a lucky break. We've sure had our share of lucky catches in the last minutes, so I had to forget it."

Landry sighed. "But it hurt. I'm dedicated to going to the Super Bowl this season, and it's my job to see that the team is dedicated to going."

He grinned over at Vic as they entered the practice field. "That's why I give tryouts to kickers who are only five years younger than I am."

Vic was embarrassed. "About my age . . ." he began.

"George Blanda was still kicking when he was forty-eight," Landry said. Vic waited for him to go on, but that was the only point Landry was making.

Brandt was already there. They joined him at the locker room, where Landry told Vic he could change clothes. The coach then went over to the equipment men and said, "Could I borrow a couple of you to snap and hold for a kicker?" Two young men quickly volunteered, one going for a bag of balls without needing to be told.

Vic came onto the field feeling a bit conscious of his paunch pushing out his T-shirt. Even so, it wasn't as bad as it once had been. Vic stood five-foot-ten, and five years ago he had been disturbed to realize he weighed 203 pounds. He didn't look fat in his clothes because it was all middle-aged belly. He liked his martinis before dinner, told friends that the only exercise he got was coughing in the morning, and ate everything on the table because he couldn't stand to see anything go to waste. Marsha Ann, to whom he had been married since 1953, had only one flaw as a cook. She overcooked. If three pork chops were left at the end of a meal, Vic ate them.

It was more than a year after Marsha Ann died that Vic reentered the almost forgotten world of dating. The girls were all younger, all were willing to spend the night, and Vic quickly decided you couldn't have an affair if you had to go around holding your stomach in. He went on a crash diet, losing fifty-five pounds in three months. He had a flat belly.

He still maintained his diet, but he was drinking more martinis and getting less exercise. In the past year he had regained twelve of those pounds, all around his middle.

Vic soon had his confidence about his physique restored as Brandt said in awe, "Where did you get those legs?"

Vic's calves, especially his right one, stood out inches from his legs, brick-hard and bulging with muscles. Vic certainly couldn't tell Brandt it was from kicking, because he hadn't kicked in thirty-eight years. He had had those calves since he was twelve years old.

So he answered, "I always say I ran away from home a lot when I was a kid."

"Where do you want to start?" Landry asked him.

"I'll start wherever you say, Coach," Vic said.

"Let's try from the thirty," Landry said.

The equipment men spilled the bag of balls out on the thirty. Vic picked one up and actually felt a thrill holding a regulation NFL ball. He recognized the big WILSON on it from TV close-ups, but discovered for the first time that it contained the signature of Pete Rozelle.

"You want to warm up?" Landry asked.

Actually, Vic did, not wanting that leg pain to return. But he was nervous. He said, "No, let's just do it."

"Right or left?" the holder asked him, kneeling on the thirty.

"Beg pardon?" Vic asked.

"You kick right-footed or left? I need to know which side to get on."

"Oh. Right, please."

The holder looked at him strangely. The other equipment man straddled the ball several yards in front of them. Landry and Brandt stood, arms folded, several yards behind and to the right side of Victor Waller.

If one had had a tape recorder going, and if such sounds as steps and a ball being twirled into place could have been recorded, the sequence would have come out sounding like this:

"Set."

Snap.

Twirl, laces out.

Step, step, step.

PONKKKK!

"Oh, did I hurt your finger?"

"No, that's all right, sir."

The holder flicked his fingers to ease the sting and turned his head to watch the ball arching through the goalposts.

No one was impressed one way or the other. Forty-yard field goals are expected in the NFL, although this guy *did* look a little long in the tooth to be making one that effortlessly.

Tom Landry said, "You want to move back to the forty or do you just want to show me what you said you can do?"

Vic pondered it. "Might as well just go for broke," he said. Adding lamely, "In the interest of time."

"Let's go back to the one," Landry said.

The equipment men gathered up the balls and walked back to the goal line. The snapper put the ball on the one and prepared to straddle it facing the goalposts.

"No," said Landry. "I meant the holder on the one. Let's turn around and go the other way."

Brandt, at Landry's side, said, "What are you saying, Tom?"

Landry indicated that the befuddled snapper should put the ball on the eight-yard line and turn his back to the near goalposts. The equally befuddled holder took his correct spot on the one, since his correct spot would now be on the *other* side of the ball if the kick—this *impossible* kick—were to go in the opposite direction.

Vic retreated three steps, entering the end zone. Then the insurance man took two more steps back for insurance.

"I'm saying," Landry muttered to Brandt, "that we're going the other way."

"He's going to make a ninety-nine-yard field goal?" Brandt asked incredulously. Then the computer man did some computing and corrected himself: "A 109-yard field goal?"

"He's going to *TRY* a 109-yard field goal," Landry said. "I only know what he claims."

"Where did you find *HIM*?" Brandt said.

"He walked into my office at three o'clock. I know nothing about him."

"How old is he, for God's sake?" Brandt asked. "Forty-five?"

"Fifty-two," Landry said.

"Fifty-two!" Brandt couldn't suppress a laugh. "That's older than Blanda when he quit!"

"I didn't say he could do it," Landry said seriously. "*He* said he could do it. I just want to watch."

They both watched. In awe. As did the snapper and holder.

Vic sailed it through from 109 yards.

History has recorded that on August 6, 1945, when the world's first atomic bomb was dropped from the *Enola Gay* on Hiroshima, the only entry in the copilot's diary was "My God!"

If history had been interested, it would have recorded that on July 7, 1982, when Victor F. Waller kicked the world's first witnessed 109-yard field goal, the equipment man/holder of the Dallas Cowboys audibly exclaimed, "Holy shit!"

Later, Vic Waller would not remember how many 109-yard field goals he kicked that July afternoon. He didn't know how many balls were in a bag. But he must have kicked ten going in that original direction and at least five more going in the other direction from the opposite end of the field. He had no misses.

Landry finally said that was enough. While Vic sat down in the end zone wishing he had a cigarette, Landry talked to Brandt at midfield.

"What do you think?" Landry asked.

"What do you mean, what do I think? I've never seen anything like it in my life."

"Neither have I," Landry said quietly. "I mean what do you think about . . . him?"

"Bad form, does everything wrong. But he gets it through without a miss."

"And . . . ?"

"We don't know what he can do against a rush."

"That can be coached."

"I know, but . . ."

"But what?"

"Well, how long can he last? What happens when one of those 270-pound kids—all of them young enough to be his son—breaks him in two?"

"We can protect him on extra points and field goals."

"Going down under kickoffs . . . ?"

Landry smiled. "I'd like to say I thought of this, but he thought of it. If you can kick 109-yard field goals, you can put any kickoff from the thirty-five out of the end zone. He doesn't have to go down when there'll never be a runback."

Brandt squinted in the sunlight. "So what do you want to do?"

Landry squinted in the sunlight. He turned to face Brandt, touching him on the arm. "Let's sign him," he said.

Landry and Brandt walked over to Vic in the end zone, and he got to his feet anxiously.

"That was amazing," Landry told him. "I'm going to leave you with Gil. And I really appreciate you coming in to see me."

Vic didn't know what he should say at this point. He said, "Thank you very much for your time, Coach Landry."

Landry said, "If you want to call me Coach Landry, that's perfectly fine with me. Some do, some don't. But please feel free to call me Tom, if you wish."

"Thanks, Tom. I don't have to tell you what a pleasure it's been to meet you."

As he walked toward his car Landry stopped the two equipment men and put an arm on each's shoulder.

"Thanks for helping us out," he told them. "I'd appreciate it if you wouldn't mention what you saw here today. Our secret, okay?"

"Okay by me, Coach," the holder said. "I don't believe what I saw, anyway."

The snapper, who also couldn't believe what he had seen, merely nodded his head. Actually, he shook his head in disbelief.

Brandt walked into the locker room where Vic was putting his three-piece suit back on and putting his shoes, shorts, and T-shirt back in his attaché case.

"We could talk right here," Brandt said, "or we could go back to my office and talk. But why don't we just talk in the car going back?"

"That's fine with me," Vic said. "Do you mind if I smoke in the car?"

As Brandt drove through the growing rush-hour traffic, and Vic Waller smoked two Kents, Brandt said he was prepared to offer Waller a contract with the Dallas Cowboys. They usually offered a minimum of $25,000 to free agents, he said, but he was prepared to offer $30,000, which was the rate the most highly rated free agents were currently getting. Brandt said he wanted to make it $30,000 because he didn't want a man to sign for less and then get to training camp and be unhappy. Vic said that was more than generous. Money was the last thing he had thought of, never dreaming that he would even be signed. He would have played for nothing, if just given the opportunity.

They went back up to Brandt's office where Gil's secretary typed in the necessary information on a standard contract. Vic signed it. Brandt told Vic training camp would start for rookies at Thousand Oaks, California, on July 18. It would last six weeks, with the veterans reporting ten days after the rookies. He said Vic would soon be receiving an airplane ticket and instructions on what he should bring to camp and be expected to do.

They shook hands and Vic took the elevator down.

Minutes later, back on the old turnpike and with the towering Dallas skyline in his rearview mirror, Victor F. Waller lit another Kent and looked at his Accutron.

Incredibly, only one hour had elapsed since he had stood at the entrance of the Dallas Cowboys' headquarters.

And he was a fifty-two-year-old Dallas Cowboy.

CHAPTER

3

As a kid in elementary school during the late 1930s, Victor Francis Waller truly loved only five things. They were, not necessarily in order, Big Little Books, Marsha Ann Reynolds, the Flash Gordon serial on the Parkway Theater's Saturday matinees, *I Love a Mystery* with Jack, Doc, and Reggie on radio, and playing baseball.

Other kids played touch football in season (no one played basketball in Texas, at least not in Vic's neighborhood) but Vic played baseball year-round, getting up games of knockout when there weren't enough for a sandlot game. He got a football one Christmas but it lay untouched atop his Big Little Books shelves. He had never seen a high school football game, couldn't remember ever listening to a college game on the radio, even those autumns when Davey O'Brien was getting national headlines in Fort Worth at nearby TCU, and had never even heard of pro football until a few days after Pearl Harbor Sunday when the newscasts told how all those government officials had been paged out of the stadium at a game in Washington, D.C.

It wasn't until he was in the seventh grade at junior high in 1942 that Vic Waller, twelve going on thirteen, found out he had a revised list of Big Five true loves. They were, still not necessarily in order, Camel cigarettes stolen from his father's carton in the kitchen cabinet, Marsha Ann Reynolds, Tuesday-night radio with Fibber McGee and Molly, Bob Hope and Red Skelton, self-abuse (the word his mother used when warning him he would go crazy if he masturbated), and playing touch football.

He still had never seen a real game, but now he listened to Southwest Conference college games on the radio every Saturday afternoon. He pumped up the sagging football on his Big Little Book shelf and played entire games by himself in the front yard, centering the ball to himself and then either running or throwing a short pass to himself until he fell down, pretending to be tackled. He changed ends in the front yard every fifteen minutes and even had a halftime when he sat on the front porch for ten minutes. Vic Waller, halfback extraordinary, played no favorites. After scoring a touchdown he became the other team and scored touchdowns for them.

The junior high crowd still played their touch games on the elementary school playground, it being devoid of yard lines and goalposts but nearer to their homes. "Three-over" for a first down, "suckers walk" after a touchdown, no extra points, and the games ended (usually in a tie) when everyone got tired. Out-of-bounds were marked by somebody's jacket and somebody else's stocking cap. The goal lines were the baseball backstop and the concrete drinking fountain, which may have been sixty yards apart but everyone told himself it was a hundred yards.

Vic, who was short and skinny, was usually chosen somewhere near last when they picked sides, until that day he caught a pass and found out he could run. He easily outraced everyone for a touchdown, and did it so consistently that he was soon being picked first. It was generally believed that Vic Waller was the fastest kid maybe in the entire city and that he would be a star when they all got to Paschal in two more years.

Now Vic loved and lived for football year-round, although he still thought the game had a dumb name. Why call it football in a game where the ball is always being run or passed? The only time the foot was used was kicking off, punting on fourth down, or for extra points. No one had ever heard of a field goal, although there may have been something said about it in *Knute Rockne, All-American*.

But Vic discovered a football hero with a foot in the fall of 1943 while listening to Texas University (no one called them the University of Texas) on the radio. He was the water boy, named Rooster Andrews, and he wasn't even 5 feet tall. He put on a uniform just to come in and kick extra points. And he did it by dropkicking, an ancient art not used anymore.

Vic soon found out he could master the precise timing of a dropkick and he spent hours practicing it. His goalpost was a curbside telephone pole with a crossbar that was used to stretch the pole's guy wire. He never missed, and now the kids were saying Vic was a cinch to be Paschal's extra-point kicker once he made the first string as a senior. There were no specialists in those days, and the kicker was always someone designated off the starting eleven. It nearly always was your senior year before you made the first string.

When Vic first heard some colleges were using a specially built kicking tee, so the holder could be free to go down the field under kickoffs, he lusted to have one. He didn't know what they looked like but he assumed they must look like those drugstore metal cups that held Coca-Cola in paper cones. The next time he was downtown he ordered a nickel Coke at the Renfro Rexall soda fountain and swiped the hourglass-shaped metal cup.

With his new and most prized possession, Vic now spent hours at the school ground doing kickoffs out of his supposed tee. He got a greater loft out of the cup, and the balls would arch from backstop goal to concrete-fountain goal. Sixty yards? Seventy?

Compliments came grudgingly from ninth-graders. But Dan (Pea Mouth) Jenkins, who stood at the other goal catching Vic's kicks and punting them (halfway) back to him, was impressed. Jenkins was the neighborhood football expert, being rich enough to go to all of TCU's home games. Although he would star in basketball, not football, at Paschal, Jenkins even then was saying his goal in life was to be a sportswriter.

"Shit fire and save matches!" Jenkins exclaimed. "That last one must've gone a hundred yards!"

Vic, who *still* hadn't seen a real game, wanted to know if that was unusual.

They never really found out how far Vic Waller could kick, or how fast he could run, when he went out for B-team football at Paschal in September of 1944. What they found out—both Vic and Jerry McCain, the B-team coach—was that Victor Waller, fourteen going on fifteen, wasn't cut out to be a football star, or even much of a player, for that matter.

At 115 pounds, he was just too little. He hated the helmet, finding it oppressively tight and hot on his head. He found he no longer had his speed in the bulky pads and cleated high-tops. And he hated to hit. He didn't mind getting hit when he had the ball—although he didn't particularly like that, either—but he had no stomach for sticking his head in there and tackling other runners. Coach McCain had placed him at left end, and in those days, of course, the same eleven played on both offense and defense. On defense Vic had to stop the end sweeps. It soon became a play that the other team began calling with gleeful regularity during practice sessions.

Vic fell from the first string to the second string, bypassed the third string entirely, stayed briefly on the fourth string, and finally settled in on the fifth string, which couldn't truthfully be called a complete string since only Vic and two other player misfits were on it. When game jerseys were issued they ran out before they got to Vic. He rationalized he was the only player with an unlisted number.

They let him practice drop-kicking extra points for a while, but that soon ended with the realization that he'd never be in the game when it was time to kick them. As for field goals, they were never practiced because high schools didn't use them. On fourth down you punted for coffin corner. If it were the last play of a tie game, you threw a long pass.

But at least he got to see his first real football games that fall. Members of the B team got free passes to the Paschal varsity games played at Farrington Field at night. And on Saturdays, Vic and his friends learned how to go over the wall at TCU home games.

The B teams played their district games on respective school practice fields in the afternoons. Vic liked to recall that the crowd always roared when he was summoned off the bench to go in at left end. They would be roaring, _"Five . . . four . . . three . . . two . . . one!"_ It was always late in the game when he got in.

The final B-team game of the season, against rival North Side, was the Big Game of the year. It was played at Paschal and the players knew varsity coach Abe Martin would be on the bench looking at his prospects for next year's A team.

Abe Martin, who was in the midst of coaching Paschal to its first district championship since the school was called Central back in the 1930s, didn't know it at the time but he wouldn't be around to coach the B-team graduates that next fall. He would go to TCU, where he would coach the Horned Frogs into the Cotton Bowl in the 1950s.

Martin was a kindly man and a "good ole country boy" whose homespun colloquialisms were legend. He fashioned several All-Americans in his time, but one fledgling left end had his career ended by one of Martin's country colloquialisms on that overcast afternoon in November of 1944. It was Victor Waller, number unlisted.

It was a day like all others to Victor Waller, taking his place on the bench. He always figured the bench would letter before he did.

And then fate stepped in.

It came in the lanky, raw-boned form of Charles (Ears) Williams, who, during the coin toss, stood on the side-lines waiting to start at left end and hawking deep into his throat for a foreign object. Ears Williams easily found the object, turned his helmeted head to spit it out, and pasted it directly on the forehead of five-foot-five B-team Coach Jerry McCain, who was standing behind him.

McCain did a slow burn, not unlike those of Edgar Kennedy in the movies, and turned angrily toward the bench, looking for the first left end he could see.

"Waller!" he shouted. "Get out there! You're starting at end."

Vic was so stunned, he tripped on the yard-marker chain as he went onto the field. Ears Williams sought anonymity in the crowd of players standing in the bench area for the kickoff.

Richard Prichard, the B-team quarterback, who was, of course, called Dick-Prick, was dismayed to see Waller trotting onto the field. Paschal had won the toss and elected to receive, and Dick-Prick had already decided he was going to call a pass to the left end on the game's first play. No one ever passed on first down, that deep in their own territory, but Dick-Prick felt the surprise ele-ment would work in his favor. And Abe Martin would surely be impressed.

Vic went down on the kickoff, failing to hit anyone from North Side. Dick-Prick had fielded the ball about on the eighteen and had gotten to the twenty before he was tackled.

Vic leaned into the huddle, suppressing a desire to introduce himself to the other players. He heard Dick-Prick saying, "PD-8-pass on three. That's you, Walker. Be ready for it."

"Waller," Vic corrected.

Vic took his stance on the line of scrimmage, thinking that PD-8-pass was, indeed, to the left end. Out eight yards and hook left, if he remembered correctly from last September.

North Side wasn't playing the pass. Vic caught it. Out in the open. No one near him.

There was absolutely nothing between him and the goal seventy yards away except grass. Sweet-smelling grass. He struck off running, the wind in his face, the crowd's roar in his ears. It was fantastic. He savored the roar as he ran.

Allowing himself a little luxury, he immediately angled across the field toward the Paschal bench so Abe Martin could get a better look at him as he went by. After all, he didn't have a number.

He could see Abe Martin there, looming in the distance. Martin was on his feet, yelling. *Wonderful moment!*

Just as Vic thundered by the bench, Martin cupped his hands to his mouth and yelled, "Score and I'll buy you a rubber dolly!"

It was the first time Martin had ever spoken to him. Vic didn't quite catch all of it. For one horrible instant he thought he might be running in the wrong direction.

Vic slammed to a shuddering, involuntary stop, turned to Martin, and said, "What, Coach?"

They say it was the first time all eleven members of a team had ever been in on the same tackle. The rolling ball of massed flesh, pads, and helmets carried Martin, the bench, and two officials with it as it skidded onto the cinder track and was obscured in a boiling cloud of dust and splinters.

It took thirty minutes after the game for them to pick all the cinders out of Vic with tweezers. At one point Dick-Prick stalked angrily past the training table and Vic looked up to say, "Well, at least we made a first down. . . ."

Vic's greatest humiliation that day had come at the game's end when he limped off the field in his tattered uniform. Paschal had lost by a touchdown, and Marsha Ann Reynolds had been in the crowd of spectators.

Marsha Ann Reynolds, whose hand he had held in the third grade, whose lips he had kissed in the seventh grade during a spin-the-bottle game at a birthday party, and whose breasts he still hadn't touched in the tenth grade, rushed up with everybody listening and said, "Vic, bring your costume over to my house tonight and I'll mend it."

A few weeks later Coach McCain told Vic what Vic already knew in his heart. Coach Martin could promote only so many players to next year's A team. That number didn't extend to the B team's fifth string. Vic, of course, could come back to the B team next fall and try again, but . . .

No one ever came back to the B team for a second year. The B team was merely the stepping-stone to the varsity. Vic decided to hang up his cleats. He had no number to be retired.

It had always been understood that Vic would someday take over his father's successful Waller Insurance Agency, so now, freed of football practice, he began working there afternoons and summers as office boy. When he graduated from Paschal he went immediately into the selling end of the agency instead of going to college.

It kept him out of Korea. Not out of the Army, of course, but out of Korea. Vic was twenty, unmarried, and 1-A in the draft when the North Koreans crossed the 38th parallel in June of 1950. He was drafted in the first wave that September. Marsha Ann Reynolds said she would wait for him. He so excelled at the complicated GI insurance segment of the clerk-typist school at Fort Dix, the Army kept him on as a cadre instructor in the course. Sergeant Victor F. Waller spent his entire two-year hitch in the Stateside chair corps.

When he came back home in September of 1952, with still nothing settled at the 38th parallel but with untold thousands of Army finance clerks well versed in the machinations of GI insurance, Vic Waller found Marsha Ann Reynolds waiting and his father dying. He married Marsha Ann in the spring of 1953, two months after Francis Waller died. Vic took over the business, quickly building it into an even bigger money-maker than it had always been.

Vic and Marsha Ann built a spacious home in the TCU area of Fort Worth and moved his widowed mother in with them. His mother died in 1956.

Except for the fact that they never had any children, no matter how mightily they tried, the Wallers were the perfect picture of the young, WASP, affluent couple—members of the Establishment before they were even thirty. They played bridge with their neighbors, penny-ante poker with old classmates on Saturday nights, and saw every movie that opened. She joined the Junior League in 1955 and he added the backyard swimming pool in 1957.

In the 1950s, Victor Waller had a revised list of Big Five true loves. They were, again not necessarily in order, Marsha Ann Waller, Kent cigarettes, movies, martinis, and pro football on black-and-white TV.

When both the new AFL Texans and the expansion NFL Cowboys presented teams to Dallas in 1960, Vic and Marsha Ann were there for at least five Texan games and maybe two Cowboy games. Vic favored the Texans, who were winners, over the hapless Cowboys, who were losers. But no matter which team was playing at home on a Sunday, the spectators in the 75,504-seat Cotton Bowl looked like marbles rolling around in a bathtub. The word was, in those days, the two teams should play each other, with the winner being allowed to leave town. They never played, but the Texans eventually left town to become the Kansas City Chiefs.

Vic eventually became a Cowboy fan, but when he told Tom Landry in 1982 that he was the Cowboys' biggest fan, he knew that wasn't correct by Tom Landry's standards. A real Cowboy fan was one who bought season tickets and sat in the stands for every home game. Vic didn't do that, but for a very good reason, he rationalized, for one so addicted to football.

If you *went* to a game, you had to miss the *other* two on TV.

If Vic's most prized possession had once been a purloined metal-cup kicking tee, it was now a TV set with a remote-control unit. He stayed welded in his den chair on fall weekends, eating in front of the TV set and clicking from game to game every time a commercial came on. It began with college games on Saturdays and ended with *Monday Night Football*. Sundays were a no-shave, marathon deal, starting at 10 A.M. with pro coaches' shows, clicking away through three pro games, and lasting until 10 P.M., when all of the Southwest Conference coaches' shows were over.

Ever since Super Bowl V he had declined to attend Super Bowl parties in the homes of friends. Marsha Ann went to the gatherings, but Vic opted to sit at home in solitary splendor where no one talked and served dip on crucial third-down plays, not paying attention to every play and every postgame locker-room quote.

How could one call himself the greatest Cowboy fan when he had never even been inside Texas Stadium, which the Cowboys had built many years ago after growing disenchanted with the Cotton Bowl?

Vic knew what he was. He was a *football* fan.

And, oddly enough, the thing he hated the most—maybe the only thing he hated about the game—was the field goal. "As dull as a field goal" was a term of comparison he frequently used. The soccer kickers had made it automatic, like the extra point. No suspense. And no touchdown.

Vic Waller had an analytical mind. His mind saw patterns in words. He worked the Jumble puzzle in the *Star-Telegram* by looking at it, not with a pencil, immediately seeing what the jumbled letters were meant to spell. He wondered why others didn't pick up on the fact that his initials, V.F.W., stood for Veterans of Foreign Wars. He loved palindromes, those words and sentences that read the same way backwards and frontwards, like "Madam, in Eden, I'm Adam." Vic thought of the perfect palindrome car: A Toyota. And why didn't others see that?

He longed to someday meet James Michener, author of *Tales of the South Pacific*, only to ask him one question. The first time Vic saw *South Pacific* on the stage, he realized that Liat, Bloody Mary's daughter who seduced Lieutenant Cable, had a name that spelled "tail" backwards. Had Michener been sitting at his typewriter and wondering, "Now what can I call this little piece of tail over on Bali Ha'i?"

Vic carried his analytical mind over into football. Everyone knew about the Super Bowl in which Miami beat Washington to become the first pro team ever to go 17–0, undefeated, in a season. They knew that Miami, leading 14–0, into the final two minutes, attempted a field goal that was blocked. Garo Yepremian, the kicker, panicked and picked up the ball to attempt a pass. It was intercepted and run back for a Washington touchdown, leaving the final score 14–7 in Miami's favor. But only Vic Waller noted that if the field goal had been good, Miami would have won its 17–0 season by a final score of 17–0.

And perhaps only Vic Waller would ask friends to figure out the symbolism of the following football situation. Vic allowed them to use a pencil to make notes, but few caught the gimmick.

"It's just the third quarter, but the Texas Longhorns are well on their way toward whipping up on TCU's Horned Frogs," Vic would begin. "The Longhorns have already scored thirty-three points, while the Frogs have only been able to muster a field goal.

"Both teams still have all their time-outs remaining, there's 4:02 remaining on the clock, and TCU has the ball, second down and goal-to-go on the Texas nine-yard line.

"The TCU quarterback takes the snap after a long count and immediately becomes the victim of a busted play. With no one to hand off to, he begins scrambling from sideline to sideline, finally even retreating up the field.

"Amazingly, he keeps getting away, and the entire play consumes twenty-nine seconds before he finally runs out-of-bounds after regaining the line of scrimmage and picking up six of the nine yards needed."

Concluded Vic, "At the precise moment when he steps out-of-bounds, something unique has happened in football. What is is?"

Most never got it. Some with pencils did. But only Vic Waller would have thought of it in the first place.

The answer: The scoreboard is frozen in all 3's.

Texas: 33.

TCU: 3.

Quarter: 3.

Time on Clock: 3:33.

Down: 3.

Yards to Go: 3.

Ball on: 3.

Texas Time-Outs Left: 3.

TCU Time-Outs Left: 3.

Vic Waller was at his office that April afternoon when the phone call came. It was exactly 2:15 P.M. by his Accutron, and the neighbor said Marsha Ann had been taken to All Saints Hospital, probably the victim of a heat stroke since she had fallen over while working in the flower beds. It wasn't a heat stroke. It was a stroke. She was dead when he got there.

That had been a little over five years ago. For four days after the funeral friends and neighbors continued to come to the house, bringing food and comfort. Then it stopped. Everyone went back to normal living, and Vic tried to. There had really never been another woman in Vic's life. He had dated a few others in high school, a few he had met while in the Army, and the one and only time he had cheated during their marriage. If you could call it cheating, when, in fact, it was a strikeout. She was married, a good friend of Marsha Ann's, one of the wives in their couples bridge club. Vic had borrowed the apartment key of a bachelor friend, and they met there, nervously, one afternoon. The first thing Vic did when they entered the apartment was straighten pictures on the wall. When it came time to perform, he found he couldn't, either because of nervousness or guilt.

Vic found their home in TCU was too big, too lonely, after Marsha Ann's death. He sold it for four times what he had paid for it and moved to an apartment on the west side in Ridgelea. He cooked for himself, continued to see every movie that opened, hibernated in front of the TV during football season, and finally went on his crash diet when he thought he might like to date again.

Like most husbands, he had often fantasized about what he would do sexually if ever single again. A different girl every night, girls who didn't want to do anything but go to bed. They were out there, all right, and they took sex and sleeping over as a matter of course. Some were divorcées or widows near his own age, but most were young girls in their twenties, quickly attracted to older men.

Vic soon found this wasn't what he wanted. They'd go to dinner or to a movie and then back to his apartment, where it was all so automatic and nonchalant. They were all on the Pill and were all on the quest for a husband. It was always the girl, not Vic, who phoned the next day. And he found he really didn't want to ask them out again. Usually he didn't, and he had a horror of running into them again and not remembering the name of someone he had slept with.

His most sobering moment came the night a newly found partner told him she was the daughter of a man Vic had gone to Paschal with. Vic asked her to please not mention their date to her parents.

Vic became more reclusive. The office was his only life, outside of TV football season. He quit taking vacations because there was no place he wanted to go by himself. He still dated, but rarely. He preferred coming home from the office, sipping his martinis as he read the evening *Star-Telegram*, and then cooking his simple dinners at his convenience. He tried to tell himself he wasn't drinking more than he used to, but he was aware that dinner kept being put off later and later.

And then one summer weekend, when *Time* magazine and *Sports Illustrated* had been read, and he had seen all the movies in town, and there was nothing on TV he wanted to see, Vic Waller sat in front of his darkened TV screen and idly wondered if he could still do what he had once done in life.

He went out and bought some kicking shoes, a tee, and a football. Then he drove to the nearby high school football field and kicked seven field goals from a distance of 109 yards. Then, like a kid who was called to dinner by his mother, he took his football and went home.

CHAPTER

....

4

Thirty miles from Los Angeles, northward up the ever-crowded four-lane Ventura Freeway, lies Thousand Oaks, California, clean, green, and sparkling in the sunshine of 85-degree summer days and bathed at night in the 65-degree breezes that roll in over the blue mountains from the nearby Pacific.

Nestled there in the Conejo Valley is tiny Cal Lutheran College, a tranquil spot of stucco buildings, shaded oak trees, and picturesque footbridges over small streams crisscrossing the campus walkways.

There is an air of old Hollywood about the subdued campus. Joel McCrea donated much of the land. Lucille Ball lives over there, and Virginia Mayo lives on the other side. The craggy mountain overlooking the two football practice fields is where John Wayne filmed *Sands of Iwo Jima*.

Tex Schramm discovered Cal Lutheran twenty years previously as the ideal summer training camp, far from the temptations of Dallas, always cool and where two-a-days had never been rained out. And for those twenty years Tom Landry had been bringing his rookie hopefuls and veterans for six weeks of trials to see just who would make the final cuts.

Don Meredith once said, "And on the seventh day, Tom said, 'Let there be Thousand Oaks.' "

There was, of course, also an air of old Cowboy legends hanging over the five dormitories, one being occupied by the coaches, two by the rookies, one by the veterans, and one by the visiting media.

This is where Walt Garrison would fill his mouth with lighter fluid, knock on a rookie's door late at night, and burst into the room spewing fire from his mouth at the terrified player.

Where Toni Fritsch sneaked out after curfew one night to buy a pizza. While returning he was stopped by a policeman who wanted to know what he was doing out at 2 A.M. Fritsch, who had no ID, could barely speak English and stood five-foot-nine and weighed two hundred pounds, couldn't make the cop believe he was a player for the Dallas Cowboys. Gil Brandt had to go down and bail Fritsch out.

And where Sam Baker, another kicker who sorely tried Landry's patience, missed a flight back from New York and didn't arrive back in camp until 3 A.M. He had to report to Landry immediately or the fine meter would continue running until he saw the coach the next day.

Dressed in a suit and holding a *New York Times* under his arm, Baker knocked on Landry's door. Landry, wearing pajamas, opened the door and saw Baker click his heels, salute, and say, "Baker reporting for duty, sir."

"Sam, that'll cost you $1,500," Landry said, closing the door.

Now, on July 18, 1982, there were eighty-nine rookies reporting to Cal Lutheran. At best, maybe seven would make the team. And that could only be accomplished by beating out several veterans, since only D. D. Lewis and Charlie Waters had retired from last year's team.

Vic Waller had been phoned by Tom Landry the day after he had signed the contract with Gil Brandt.

"Have you told Dan Jenkins, or any other sportswriter, yet about signing with us?" the coach wanted to know.

"No, I haven't. And Dan doesn't even know I was the kicker who wanted the tryout," Vic answered.

"Well, I know you'll want to tell him," Landry said, "and I know there'll be a lot of news value connected to it, considering your age and the fact you never played in college."

"Yes, I suppose so. . . ."

"The thing I'd like to ask of you," Landry continued, "is to not mention to him, or anyone, the distance you get. Or your success rate." Landry laughed. "They probably wouldn't believe it anyway, and it might be better to let these things come out as they happen."

"Sure, Tom. I agree."

"See you in Thousand Oaks," Landry said.

It was, indeed, an amazing story that Vic told Dan when he got him on the phone. "Shit! Now I'll have to come out to Thousand Oaks to do a piece on you," Jenkins said. "I promised myself years ago that I'd never go to another Catholic stand-up wedding or to another concentration camp where jocks throw Coke machines down the dorm stairs."

Vic also felt an obligation to phone the news to an old Fort Worth poker-playing buddy, *Star-Telegram* sports columnist Galyn Wilkins. Wilkins wrote an excellent column about Vic that was soon picked up by the wire services.

The headline on Wilkins's column read:

INSURANCE MAN GETS
EVERYMAN'S DREAM

Vic turned over his business to Andy Freeman, his number one associate, shut up his apartment, and was driven to the D/FW airport that Sunday by Freeman and his wife.

Upon arrival at LAX, he had been instructed to watch for Cal Lutheran student athletes who were meeting all the planes at the various terminals. They would all be wearing staff T-shirts with DALLAS COWBOYS on the front.

Vic checked in with the first two he saw at the Delta terminal. They checked off his name on their lists, got his luggage on a waiting bus, told him they'd be leaving as soon as they had a full load, and called him "sir." They thought he was an assistant coach.

It wasn't so much that Vic was the oldest man on the bus. It was that he was the smallest, dwarfed by the huge college athletes who soon filled up the Greyhound. Vic sat at the rear, looking out the back window at the endless stream of cars behind them in all four lanes. It looked like they were being chased by a posse.

The dorm rooms looked rather spartan to Vic, who had never been inside a college dorm. But his roommates, all of whom had, assured him that Cal Lutheran was the most lavish they had ever encountered. There were three rooms to a suite, each room containing two bunk-type beds, two dressers, two desks, and no telephones. It would house six students in the fall, but because of the size of pro football players, the Cowboys assigned only four men to a suite.

Rookies were assigned to rooms alphabetically, and Vic shared a third-floor suite with a running back from Wyoming named Williams, an offensive guard from Tulane named Walker, and a defensive back from Purdue named Watson.

To a man, they all thought Vic was an assistant coach— until they were surprised to see him being issued a practice uniform along with everyone else. Rookies were allowed to request jersey numbers if they were not already taken. Vic asked for, and got, number 3. Symbolic, his analytical mind told him, of a field goal's points.

Their days began at 7:15 A.M. when The Turk would push open the door and sing out, "Rise 'n' shine, babies." He was a short, squat, rotund black man, a Cal Lutheran student whose real name was never learned by the rookies. He was called The Turk because later it would be his job on those "Rise 'n' shine, babies" mornings to tell the players, "Coach Landry wants to see you in his room. Bring your playbook." And the bearer of this bad news, that a player was to be cut, was called The Turk in all NFL training camps.

They went to breakfast in the campus cafeteria at 7:30 A.M., wearing T-shirts and shorts. Attendance was mandatory, players being required to sign in whether they ate or not. Vic was impressed by the food, his diet disbanded to the unlimited quantities of eggs, bacon, sausage, ham, cereal, hotcakes, and fruit. Always fruit. He marveled at always seeing Tom Landry leaving the cafeteria with a bunch of grapes, dour-faced offensive line coach Jim Myers leaving with a *box* of grapes.

Then came taping by the trainers, the donning of the uniform, which Vic felt uncomfortable and foolish in. The helmet was still oppressively hot and tight, and the Cowboys had a rule about not taking it off to sit on. But if Vic Waller felt foolish in the Cowboy silver and blue, he soon found he didn't look foolish. Kickers were expected to be small. Wearing glasses under the face mask was no longer considered unusual in the NFL. He was accepted. As a *kicker*, that is. All kickers were considered to be crazy. The last Cowboy kicker to be considered sane was Mike Clark, Vic was told seriously one day by Joe Bailey, the Cowboys' young and handsome vice president in charge of administration. "And you know how long that's been," Bailey added.

Morning practice was from 10 A.M. to noon, with the offense and defense using opposite ends of one practice field, and the small group of kickers and punters working lonesomely by themselves on the second field. Lunch, with the players back in T-shirts and shorts, was always heavy on the cold cuts. More taping, then back on the fields from 3 P.M. to 5:30. Dinner, featuring steak, chicken, and ribs, was from 6:00 to 7:30. Then came the team meetings, lasting until 9:30, where smoking was tolerated but dozing off during the films wasn't. Curfew was 11 P.M.

The veterans reported ten days later, and so did the spectators. Families took vacations to watch America's Team at Thousand Oaks, and up to a thousand people from all over the nation were in the bleachers every day for the two-a-days. At the lunch breaks huge throngs of teenagers and younger kids stood outside the cafeteria asking for player autographs, not sure who their heroes were since they weren't wearing jersey numbers.

One day Vic happened to be walking behind Tony Dorsett and Harvey Martin, who didn't need numbers to be recognized, and had to wait as the autograph-seekers surrounded the pair at the cafeteria door. One teenage girl asked Vic for his autograph.

He was flattered to be included, but felt compelled to tell the girl, "You don't want my autograph. I'm not anybody."

"You're an assistant coach, aren't you?" the girl said. "Sign."

Each Wednesday a check for $300 was delivered to the players, and Wednesday was a night off, meaning no team meetings after practice. The Four W's, as Vic and his roommates came to dub themselves, had rented a car for their six-week stay and would avail themselves of Thousand Oaks's better restaurants and movie theaters on Wednesday nights.

Vic had martinis while his younger companions drank beer. Vic got misty-eyed when they saw *An Officer and a Gentleman*. The other three W's said they preferred the movie they had all taken in the week before, *Young Doctors in Love*.

Vic ended up paying for the rental car before the six weeks were up, because he had the dorm suite all to himself.

Although he didn't talk their language, or share their tastes in music, Vic had come to like the three W's, and now, as The Turk came calling, he wished he hadn't come to know them so well. He felt like Gregory Peck not wanting to know about the girlfriends and dreams his bomber crews had as he sent them out on missions over Germany.

Walker was the first to be told Coach Landry wanted to see him and to bring his playbook.

When the shaken youth came back to the room, the others wanted to know what Landry had said.

"He thanked me for coming, but said he just didn't think I was NFL caliber."

Watson was next. "He thanked me for coming and said he thought I could make it somewhere else in the NFL, but not with the Cowboys."

Williams lasted four weeks, and was beginning to think he was going to survive. When he came back to the room that morning, he sat on the side of the bed and cut the narrative to Vic down to one word: "Shit."

The Turk, ever oblivious to the room's dwindling occupants, continued to wake Vic up every morning with "Rise 'n' shine, babies." Still plural.

Vic told him one morning, "You're never going to get me, Turk."

"How so?" The Turk grinned.

"I'm a kicker," Vic said. "I don't have a playbook to turn in."

CHAPTER

. . . .

5

The kicker on the University of New Mexico football team was no specialist, just a big, beefy lineman who doubled on kickoffs, extra points, and field goals.

In the off-season he wrestled huge barrels of syrup at the Coca-Cola plant in Albuquerque, loading them onto a freight elevator and sitting atop them for the ride up.

His right foot, his kicking foot, was dangling six inches over the edge of the open-gate freight elevator as it approached the concrete beam stretched between each floor of the plant.

As the groaning elevator passed the beam it sliced off the junior tackle's toes.

In the hospital the doctor said grimly, "They tell me you're the team's kicker."

"Just trim 'em up even," the football player said.

He was in the hospital thirteen days, and then left school for the remainder of the semester to recover at his California home in Long Beach.

It was the sand of the beach that he wanted to run in. He packed his right football shoe with cotton to fill the area where his toes had been. And as he ran it became less painful and he knew he would be able to play football again in his senior year.

No one ever assumed he would kick again.

The first ball he kicked on the beach was painful. The pain lessened with each ensuing kick. On his seventh kick there was no pain because his foot was numb.

When he went home and took off his shoe the cotton was a mass of blood.

The overlapping skin was too close to the bone, so he waited for it to heal up again. Then he went back out and kicked until the blood started again.

He kicked for two months, and finally the toughened skin held.

Ben Agajanian went back to college that fall, was outfitted with a shortened box-toe shoe, and kicked and played his way into the pros.

Like most good kickers, Agajanian was called Golden Toe in the newspapers. Few realized there were no toes.

He played for the Eagles, the Steelers, the Giants, the Rams, the Chargers. And when he became too old to play in the line, he became the game's first kicking-only specialist. In 1961, when he was kicking for the old Dallas Texans, he was a commuter, flying in for Sunday games and going back to Long Beach that night.

A would-be kicker once asked Ben how he could get a kicking shoe like his.

"First," said Agajanian, "you get a hatchet . . ."

He kicked until he was forty-five ("Blanda beat me by three years"), built up a successful string of sporting-goods stores, and then sold them to live the good life of retirement in Long Beach.

Ben Agajanian was sixty-three that summer morning in 1982 when he drove his Rolls-Royce into Thousand Oaks to begin his annual stint as the Cowboys' special kicking coach. For several years he had been guiding the kickers through training camp and the preseason gamers. When the final cuts had been made he would stay on in Dallas for a couple of weeks into the regular season working with the chosen kicker. Then he would go back home for the

rest of the season unless called back to work out any
problems the kicker might have developed.

Agajanian was a friendly bear of a man who would have
been called Gentle Ben even if there had never been that
TV series. Most people called him Aggie. Tom Landry
called him Benjamin, only because Ben called Landry
Thomas.

"Benjamin," Landry said to him that first morning,
"we've got a little surprise for you out there. A kicker
who's never played before, and he's fifty-two." Landry,
who never laughed when he talked football, didn't think it
was necessary to add "Don't laugh" before he went on.

"We think he's good, and I'd like to know what you
think as soon as possible. His name is Waller. Don't work
him too hard, and don't try him beyond the thirty."

Two days later Agajanian set his lunch tray down
beside Landry at the coaches' table.

"What can I say, Thomas? He does everything wrong
and he has no form. But he gets 'em through."

"Had him from the thirty yet?"

Ben nodded. "He made it easy. But that's another
thing, Thomas. He hasn't missed a single one yet."

Landry didn't change his expression, but then again
Agajanian didn't expect him to.

"We'll have to see how he does against the rush,"
Landry said.

The rush wouldn't come until after the veterans reported to training camp.

In those first ten days of camp Vic had been a natural
for lunchtime interviews with the media. The *Star-Telegram*
and both Dallas papers did big features on him, and
Verne Lundquist interviewed him for Channel 8.

Vic and two other free-agent kickers spent their two-a-
days learning the fundamentals of kicking from Ben.

Greg Porter of TCU and David Finzer of DePauw had
no illusions about making the Cowboy team. Not with

Rafael Septien being All-Pro and leading the league with 121 points on twenty-seven of thirty-five field goals and forty of forty extra-point tries. They were just thankful for the chance to work out with the Cowboys, play in the exhibition games, be seen by other scouts, and perhaps be picked up by other teams when the inevitable cuts came.

Ben liked Vic, perhaps feeling closer to him because of their ages. He liked Waller's honesty and sincerity. "Aggie, I don't even know what they say in the huddle," Vic told him that first day.

"When you get out there you won't even be in the huddle," Ben said. "You'll be lining up the angle. There's no snap count on extra points or field goals, so in the huddle the holder just tells the center 'Snap it when I'm ready.' "

"I never knew there wasn't a snap count. How does the line keep from jumping offsides before the ball comes back?"

Ben explained patiently. "The line won't jump because they're defending against the rush. They're stepping backward to take on the rush."

Victor Waller, armchair football expert, had never thought of that.

"The holder kneels seven yards behind the center. You'll be three steps behind him. The holder will look at you and ask if you're ready. When you nod he'll turn to the center and hold his hands out. That means he's ready, and the ball is snapped at the center's discretion. After placing the ball the holder never looks up, only at the ball."

Aggie grinned. "The Cowboys actually set the ball down seven yards and two feet back. I found out a long time ago you needed an extra yard to get an angle up and over the rushers' arms. Eight yards would be best, but you know why I told 'em seven yards and two feet?"

Vic shook his head.

"If I'd said take it back a full yard, Tom would've said 'Oh, Benjamin, you're tampering with the standards of the game.' But seven yards and two feet sounds scientific."

Ben never worked his trio of kickers very hard. He never ran them through the ropes or sent them to strength coach Bob Ward's "torture machines," the elaborate weight-lifting equipment that every other player had to use at the end of each day's practice. "Kickers don't need it," Ben said. "And they could pull something or get injured."

Agajanian knew a kicker could only kick for so long and loosen up in stretching exercises for just so long. His three pupils would alternate snapping and holding for one another, while a band of subteen boys from Thousand Oaks eagerly shagged the balls. Often the kickers would spend time throwing passes to one another. Vic occasionally caught one.

And often they spent a lot of time just sitting on the grass, a tiny little group alone on their own practice field, envied by the rest of the rookies, who were sweating and pounding out their lives on the adjacent field.

"One day several years ago," Aggie told Vic, "the camera guys on the tower would turn their cameras after each play and shoot us sitting on the grass. They showed 'em in the team meeting that night and it brought down the house.

"Everybody laughed, but I still kinda worried about it, so I went to a couple of the team leaders like Bob Lilly and Craig Morton and asked them if they resented us having it so easy. Morton said, 'Just so it goes through the uprights, we don't care what you do.'

"Still, I decided to get them out of sight during the afternoons, and that's when I started them jogging up in the mountains." He pointed toward John Wayne's "Iwo Jima."

"I had to quit it, though. Toni Fritsch didn't come back one afternoon so I went up there looking for him. I found him sitting on a rock drinking a six-pack of beer. All that time he'd been driving up there at night and leaving a six-pack in a cooler for the next day."

Vic laughed as he sat beside Ben in the shaded golf cart that was one of the two perks Ben had over the other assistant coaches. His other perk was having his own cottage apartment on the campus rather than sharing a room in the coaches' dorm.

"I had to have it," Ben told Vic. "I snore. I mean I snore loud, and can't stop it. It was always driving the other guy crazy, but it was bothering me more because I never knew when I was doing it and I was getting too nervous wondering how bad I was making it for a roommate."

It was in Ben's cottage that the kickers held their nightly team meetings, watching films of their own kicking and the styles and forms of other NFL kickers.

And it was there that Vic met Rafael Septien when the veterans reported to camp.

He burst through the door in a rush of joyful emotion, hugging Agajanian and shouting over and over, "Uncle Ben! Uncle Ben! Have you missed me? I've missed you."

The two had genuine affection for one another, and Vic asked Ben one day if anyone else called him Uncle Ben.

"Only my nephews," Aggie said.

Septien was a deceptively slim young man, darkly handsome with his narrow mustache and curly black hair, happily in love with his recently wed wife, deeply religious, and a member of the Cowboy Bible study group that included linebackers Bob Breunig and Guy Brown, guard Herb Scott and running back James Jones.

Septien was a quiet young native of Mexico City who rarely engaged in small talk. He accepted Vic—although he asked Vic not to smoke in the nightly meetings—just as he accepted Greg Porter and David Finzer. He knew no one was going to take his job away from him. However, Rafael began to realize after a few days that Vic never missed on his kicks.

Now Agajanian was taking his four kickers to afternoon sessions on the second field, working with regular center Tom Rafferty and backup quarterback Glenn Carano, who would be the holder replacing the retired Charlie Waters.

It was here, standing on the sidelines while waiting for "their" team to be waved in, that Vic finally began to get the up-close feel of pro football. For the first time he began to feel that he was actually a Dallas Cowboy.

He wandered the sidelines like a tourist, moving from group to group where offensive and defensive groups worked out under the various assistant coaches. Jerry Tubbs, bundled in a windbreaker trying to sweat off pounds as he gently explained how linebackers should tear off heads. Ernie Stautner actually getting down and mixing it with his padded young giants. Dick Nolan prowling in front of his receivers as they strained through stretching exercises on the grass, trying to detect whether the mutterings Butch Johnson was making to Jay Saldi were dirty remarks about him.

"What are you saying, Butch?" Nolan barked at the wide receiver.

"Just talkin' about *them*, Coach," Johnson returned, waving his arm in the general direction of two teenage girls among the distant crowd of spectators.

Everyone knew who he meant. The girls had been the talk of the training camp that day, prancing around the team attired in string bikinis. One of them was bending into an open car window now, the string disappearing into her upturned buttocks. The girls were sixteen, tops.

"Call their bluff, Butch," said Saldi, bending his head toward his outstretched leg. "Call their damn bluff."

"I'll call their fathers, that's who I'll call," Johnson said as he bent his head in the exercise. "They're *crazy*, coming here with all these horny men around!"

"Miss Herpes, 1982," Saldi said.

Overlooking all the groups, and never missing a thing, stood the commanding figure of Tom Landry, dressed in billed cap, gold shirt, blue shorts, and football shoes. A whistle hung from his neck and an ever-present white bullhorn was held in his hand.

Vic marveled at the brute strength of Randy White during defensive line drills. White wasn't tall and he didn't look all that big close up, but he was the strongest man on the Cowboy team. What looked like a beer belly— but wasn't—hung out of his half-jersey and over his belt. There hadn't been a 54 practice jersey and they had given White a 64 that now read just 4. White had ripped off the 6, saying he didn't want anyone thinking he was Tom Rafferty.

When they had goal-line stand scrimmages, Vic was surprised to hear all those loud and painful grunts and groans that until now he had assumed were just dubbed-in sound tracks on those NFL Films television shows. And when Tony Dorsett or Ron Springs would smash head-on into the likes of Randy White, John Dutton, and Bob Breunig in explosions that seemed to rock the very ground of the sidelines, Vic vowed he would never again criticize any player for fumbling. How they held on to the ball was beyond him.

Vic, of course, was the only rookie who was seeing all this for the first time. He gloried in watching Danny White bring the team out of the huddle on passing drills, barking "Red! Forty-three! Hut, hut" or "Blue! Eighty-one! Hut, hut," the signals that would reveal whether or not an audible was being called.

Vic was a gawker and, as such, got run over on the sidelines once when White sent a long soarer toward the sidelines to Drew Pearson, who was being matched step-by-step by cornerback Everson Walls. The pass went incomplete, but momentum carried both Pearson and Walls into

Vic. He went to the ground, and for the first time realized the value of his pads.

From the far end of the field Landry raised the bullhorn to his lips and Vic heard the raspy words: "Let's learn to stay back from the sidelines, Vic."

Kickoff coverage and field-goal rush were the last items of the day before the team wound up practice with wind sprints and a session on Bob Ward's "torture machines."

When he stood there ten yards behind the *real* Dallas Cowboys, his arm raised waiting for the whistle to kick, and looking downfield at another team of *real* Cowboys waiting to return it, Vic suddenly felt he was at last a *real* Cowboy. Number 3, silver helmet and all.

Kicking from the thirty-five, he of course sent the ball out of the end zone.

The ten men charging down the field pulled up short and returned to the thirty-five. Somebody placed another ball on the tee.

Which Victor Waller immediately kicked out of the end zone again.

Tom Landry's voice, with a touch of irritation in it, rasped over the bullhorn, "How can I have a kickoff coverage drill, Vic, if the ball's not in the field of play?"

"Just trying to make the team, Coach." Vic smiled at Landry.

He got no smile in return.

The next one Vic managed to place in someone's waiting arms on the five-yard line. The minute the ball left his toe Vic was startled to hear the Cowboys on each side of him yelling, "Fight! Fight!"

Vic trotted to the sidelines, per instructions, and asked Ben, "What are they yelling 'fight' for? I don't see any fight."

Aggie said, "They're telling each other 'right.' Your kick went to the right side of the field. If it goes to the left side, they'll yell 'left.'"

Later, when it came time for Vic's first field-goal attempt against the rush, he felt a new sensation standing behind *real* Cowboys and facing—much closer—other *real* Cowboys. He not only was nervous, but, for the first time, he was scared.

He was kicking last. Septien and Porter had made their field goals from the twenty. Finzer had missed his to the left.

Tom Landry leaned into the defensive huddle, speaking softly. "Two things on this next kick," he said. "There's a fine in it for anybody who hits the kicker. And, second, I want it blocked."

The kicking team took its stance. Glenn Carano knelt on his spot and asked Vic if he was ready. Vic nodded. Carano stretched out his arms toward Rafferty.

Vic watched the ball spiral back and, almost like it was in slow motion, saw Carano place it down and twirl the laces to the front. Vic took his three steps and swung his foot.

BLOCKED!

The sound of the ball being slapped by the huge arms of Too Tall Jones sounded like an explosion to Vic. The ball was flopping around on the ground somewhere behind Vic. No one was even going after it since it was just a drill.

"That's what we've got to work on," Landry said quietly to Agajanian.

"I see what he did wrong, Thomas. We can fix it."

Agajanian pulled Vic, Carano, and Rafferty aside. "Starting tomorrow," he said, "we move the holder back that extra foot whenever Vic kicks."

Landry had quietly passed the word for all the coaches to remain on the field after all the players—and reporters—had gone in. He told Agajanian to keep Waller and a bag of balls on the field.

After the last of the spectators had driven away, Landry called the group together under the goalposts and asked

Agajanian to hold for Vic on the one-yard line—going the other way.

Agajanian was surprised, but he never questioned Landry.

Landry said to Vic, "All right. Let's see you do what you did back in Dallas."

Vic took his place, took his steps, and took a niche in football history. The ball went through the uprights 109 yards away.

The reaction of the amazed coaches was the same as it had been for Landry, Gil Brandt, and the equipment men back in Dallas that day. Some shouted, some expressed awed obscenities, most exclaimed they didn't believe what they had seen. Gene Stallings could only drawl, "What's that guy's name?"

Ben Agajanian, the most startled of them all, couldn't say anything. He could only look at Vic in amazement.

Finally, aging coach said to aging pupil, "Do you do that every time?"

Vic said, "So far, Aggie, so far."

Landry had him kick two more from the same spot. They both went through. Several of the coaches came up to shake Vic's hand. He looked a little too long in the tooth for a high-five.

"Since I had everyone go in before we did this," Landry told the coaches, "I assume you know I don't want this talked about."

Jim Myers, whose official title was assistant head coach, looked at the others and said, "Better believe it."

Vic rode off with Agajanian in the golf cart. He never again had a kick blocked. If Landry noticed that the holder was not eight yards back, he never mentioned it to Agajanian.

Midway in the fourth week of training camp Landry made the decision to keep Vic Waller as his kicker. The problem was what to do about Rafael Septien.

"I wouldn't want to trade him to any team we'd be playing in our conference," Gil Brandt said to Landry. "You don't want the best—or second-best—kicker in the business coming back to beat you."

"I've thought about that," Landry said. "But how can they beat us if we know we're going to win?"

Brandt thought that over for a moment. "What if Waller goes sour? Or steps off a curb and breaks his leg?" he asked.

"What if Rafael breaks *his* leg?" Landry countered. "Nobody can afford the luxury of carrying two kickers."

Which, of course, Brandt knew.

Two days before the team was to fly back to Dallas for its first exhibition game, a Saturday-night sellout against Buffalo that would be on national TV, Landry held his weekly after-lunch press conference in the game room of the coaches' dorm.

Doug Todd, the Cowboy public relations director, had already flown back to Dallas to handle the press coming in for the game. His assistant, Greg Aiello, was handling the Thousand Oaks press conference.

Aiello, a lithe and handsome New Yorker, had been surprised earlier that morning to receive a phone call from Landry wanting some information about the 1972 Miami Dolphins, the team that went undefeated to a 17–0 season.

"Can you find out for me what the Dolphins' preseason record was that year?" the coach asked. "I'm sure they weren't undefeated there, too, or we would have remembered it."

Aiello thought he'd have to phone his counterpart at Miami, but he found the information in the Dolphins' annual press book.

"They played six exhibition games in those days," Greg said when he called Landry back, "and they went 3–3. They lost to Detroit, then lost—"

"Thanks, Greg," Landry said. "That's all I needed to know."

Now as Aiello walked with Landry from the cafeteria to the game room, where the reporters were already seated, he was struck with an impish thought. "Wait here at the door, Tom, and let me go in first," he said.

Aiello entered the buzzing room and announced stiffly, "All rise."

The room erupted in laughter as the grinning Landry walked in and took a seat behind a desk.

The first questions were about Buffalo. And then came questions about the Cowboys.

Glenn Carano had injured his knee in camp, and, if doctors said he could play again later in the season, Landry said he'd begin the season with just two healthy quarterbacks, Danny White and Gary Hogeboom. Ken Sins of the *Star-Telegram* wanted to know who would play quarterback if both White and Hogeboom were injured in the same game.

"Well, Tony Hill, Drew Pearson, or Dennis Thurman," Landry said, smiling. "They all think they're quarterbacks."

Jim Dent of the Dallas *Times Herald* reminded Landry that before training camp Landry had publicly challenged Harvey Martin and Drew Pearson, both thirty-one, to rekindle their enthusiasm toward football. How had they been doing?

"They're working hard, and both are having good camps," Landry said. "Listen, when you reach thirty, every year you have to rededicate yourself. That goes for the coach too. This is a hard business, and you've got to get your mind set right and really want to play."

Midway through the press conference Tex Schramm had entered the room and taken a seat in the back. Now, as he saw the session slowly winding down, the Cowboy president and general manager walked to the front and stood beside Landry's chair.

"Your editors back home already have this on the wire, but I wanted to tell you about an announcement that was made today," Schramm began. "The league has voted to expand the rosters from forty-five to forty-nine men, the extra four being carried on an inactive roster. They can be activated from week to week, so long as they are replaced by four others on the inactive list."

Verne Lundquist of Channel 8 asked Landry how he felt about the change.

"Well, I like it, I'll tell you right now, because it means we can have more football players," Landry said. "A coach is always looking for more football players."

Jim Dent thought to himself that it was probably a ploy by the NFL to dilute the talent pool for the upcoming United States Football League, but he didn't voice the opinion. He also thought that it looked as if Landry was hearing the news for the first time, but he couldn't be sure.

Tom Landry didn't say. But he knew a decision had been made for him.

He would keep Rafael Septien.

CHAPTER

....

6

Tom Landry was steaming. Not steaming like the 65,000 fans who were baking in the 100-degree heat of Texas Stadium, but steaming because the Dallas Cowboys were getting beat by an inferior team in front of a sellout crowd and a national TV audience.

Inside the final two-minute warning period, Buffalo was leading the Cowboys 14–10, and the Cowboys, like they had been doing all the second half, were stalling out.

Dorsett had run nine yards for a touchdown on the last play of the first quarter, and Septien had kicked a forty-eight-yard field goal in the second to give the Cowboys a 10–0 lead. And then nothing. There had been no Cowboy offense at all in the second half, and plenty of fumbles and interceptions. But Buffalo had five scoring drives, missing on three field-goal attempts and scoring two touchdowns.

Landry had let Septien, Porter, and Finzer alternate on the kickoffs, but Vic hadn't gotten into the game. Waller stood on the sidelines next to Agajanian, still mesmerized by the awesome blue aura of Texas Stadium, the incredible ever-enveloping noise of the crowd, the furnacelike heat of an August night pouring through the famed hole in the roof.

Up in the press box Galyn Wilkins of the Fort Worth *Star-Telegram* had already started his column:

"Saturday night's Cowboy opener against the Bills was a typical Fricassee and Fumble Fiesta. For 15 bucks they stick you in a Dutch oven called Texas Stadium, cook you three and half hours at 100 degrees and baste you with fumbles, misplays, penalties and third-string quarterbacks."

Nearby, Frank Luksa of the Dallas *Times Herald* began his lead with "The Cowboys were cold on a hot night."

Neither story would see print.

Landry had come to a decision. A very un-Landry-like decision, one that flew in the face of everything he had stood for all these years. He wanted to *win*, no matter what it took. Forget that this was just an exhibition game. Forget that the purpose of these games was just to test the rookies. Forget that he had always been critical of Lombardi's obsession to win these meaningless games because they sold tickets. Tom Landry didn't need to sell tickets, but he needed to win!

Now only thirty seconds remained on the clock, and just two-thirds of the crowd remained in the stands. And another Danny White pass had been dropped on second down.

On third and eight from their own thirty-five, Landry turned to the bench and shouted, "Field-goal team be ready." Then to Agajanian he said, "I want to use Waller."

The field-goal team couldn't believe what they heard. From their own end of the field? And they needed a touchdown, not a field goal, to win!

A long pass to Tony Hill was over the receiver's head. Fourth down and twenty-three seconds left on the clock.

"Field-goal team in," Landry said.

While Glenn Carano was recovering from his knee injury, Gary Hogeboom was doing the holding. Agajanian grabbed Hogeboom's shoulder pad and said, "Remember. Eight yards." To Vic he said, "Relax and just do it like all the others."

Up in the broadcast booths, they couldn't believe it. "The punting team is coming in," Pat Summerall said in a puzzled tone. "I don't know why Landry wouldn't go for another pass."

"It's a fake," John Madden said. "Danny White's the punter. He'll pass. It won't fool Buffalo."

"Wait a minute," Summerall said. "White came out. And Hogeboom is kneeling. They're going for a field goal! From their own thirty-five! Hogeboom is kneeling on the twenty-seven, it looks like. What'll that be? *Eighty-three yards!*"

"I don't have to look up the record," Madden said, his voice beginning to rise. "The record is sixty-three yards by Tom Dempsey."

"The kicker is going to be Vic Waller," Summerall said, looking at the Cowboy numerical roster. "That's the fifty-two-year-old free agent you may have read about. He's a Fort Worth insurance agent who hasn't played football since high school! I don't believe any of this!"

Over in the radio booth, Verne Lundquist and Brad Sham were doing their own computing and making their own excited observations.

Lundquist was laughing. "Hogeboom was the big talk of training camp. He renegotiated his contract for $900,000 over three years. What we've got out there is a $300,000 holder and a fifty-two-year-old kicker."

"A $300,000 holder who is also a quarterback," Sham reminded. "It's a fake. Hogeboom will pick it up and pass."

"That's what Buffalo believes," Lundquist said. "They didn't even put their special team in. They're in regular pass defense."

The crowd roar was so loud, Vic couldn't even hear Hogeboom ask if he was ready. He could only read his lips and nod.

The ball came back and Hogeboom placed it down. Vic took his three steps and kicked.

The long, long, lazily drifting kick would be replayed countless times on countless TV shows in the coming hours, days, and week. Of all the stunned millions watching in disbelief, no two people were more stunned than Rafael Septien and the official who raised his arms over his head at the far end of the field.

Pandemonium broke loose.

"IT'S GOOD! IT'S GOOD!" Summerall was shouting.

"IT WON'T COUNT IN THE RECORDS," Madden was screaming. "LEAGUE RECORDS COUNT ONLY IN REGULAR SEASON GAMES. DEMPSEY STILL HAS IT AT SIXTY-THREE!"

"FOR THE FIRST TIME IN MY BROADCAST CAREER I REALLY DON'T KNOW IF YOU CAN HEAR ME OVER THIS CROWD! I CAN'T HEAR MYSELF," Summerall chanted.

On the field Vic was being mobbed, buried, by about an even ton of Cowboys. Underneath the pile, he actually worried that he might suffocate.

The director in the CBS truck opted not to cut away for commercials, focusing on the ever-growing roar of the standing crowd, the jubilation on the Cowboy bench, the disbelief of the Buffalo bench, the hugging, jumping high-fiving Cowboys on the field.

A Cowboy equipment man was credited for retrieving the ball in the end zone and saving it for Vic Waller. It would later end up in the Pro Football Hall of Fame at Canton, Ohio.

On the sidelines Landry was somehow making himself heard over the din: "Onside-kick team in!" he was shouting.

Buffalo was ready for *this* one. Everyone watching across the nation was too.

Rafael Septien, surrounded by the sure-handed backs and receivers of the special team, couldn't hear the official's whistle for him to begin the kick and had to be signaled to advance on the ball.

It was a perfect execution of football's most difficult play.

The ball went exactly ten yards, was muffed by a Buffalo lineman, and the Cowboys' Ron Fellows fell on it.

More pandemonium.

The clock automatically stopped for the change of offensive and defensive teams.

Landry grabbed Danny White and shouted to him, "Fall down with it, and then tell the referee to call time out when the clock runs down to three seconds!"

Then to the bench he yelled: "Field-goal team be ready. Waller."

White's knee touched down two yards behind the line of scrimmage. And so, with three seconds remaining and the ball on the Cowboys' forty-three, Vic Waller calmly kicked a seventy-five-yard field goal that went through on the final tick of the clock.

Cowboys 16, Buffalo 14!

Up in the booths they were going crazy. Down on the field the entire team was now mobbing Vic. In the stands they were screaming with the incredible zeal of fans who were realizing they had seen football history made.

Tom Landry's secret weapon was no longer a secret.

CHAPTER

....

7

While Vic Waller had become an overnight sensation with just two swings of his foot that Saturday night, it took a little more time for him to become a nationwide celebrity of superstar proportions.

Roughly, two weeks.

Virtually every newspaper in the country, from the *New York Times* right on down, used their Sunday front pages, as well as the sports pages, to carry Vic's picture and news stories of the historic event.

Because Dan Jenkins had flown into Thousand Oaks earlier to do an in-depth piece on his old hometown friend, Vic made the cover of *Sports Illustrated*.

For three nights they had sat in restaurants reminiscing about their years in Fort Worth, laughing about Vic's idiosyncrasies, remembering "the time that . . ."

Dan got Vic to do his routines about the old days of network radio, all the time nursing his J&B-water and his ever-present cups of coffee and never taking a note.

But when Jenkins went back to his room to write, he produced a flawless nine-pager that informed the world of a human, warm, and witty Vic Waller, not just a middle-aged robot in a silver helmet.

The *Sports Illustrated* cover was cleverly titled OLDEN TOE.

Reporters, magazine writers, TV camera crews, and even the foreign press had surged into Thousand Oaks. *People* captioned its cover "V" AS IN VICTOR(Y). *Time*'s two-page feature was headlined AS DULL AS A FIELD GOAL?

So great was the Vic Waller impact on pro football, the Cowboys became the first team in NFL history to have all their exhibition games on national TV. NBC chose to telecast the San Diego game, and CBS quickly opted to do the New England and the Houston games. And because ABC had already scheduled America's Team on *Monday Night Football* for the regular season opener, the Cowboys became the first team ever to appear on national TV five times in a row.

Tom Landry didn't let the networks down. Even though the next three games still were only exhibitions, he used Vic on every kickoff (none of which was ever returned) and every long-range field goal (none of which was ever missed). He sent in Septien only on extra points and chip-shot field goals.

Waller kicked field goals of fifty-five, sixty-seven, and sixty yards as the Cowboys beat the Chargers 37–16 in San Diego. Back in Dallas for the third game, he had a seventy-nine-yarder as the Cowboys beat the Patriots 37–21. And against Houston in Texas Stadium, Vic won the game 17–14 with a sixty-six-yarder that Tom Landry almost waited too long to call.

But when he turned out to be one of the most interesting guests ever interviewed by Johnny Carson on *The Tonight Show*, Vic's fate was sealed as a man destined never again to go unrecognized in public.

Carson scheduled Vic just before the Cowboys broke camp at Thousand Oaks. He was so sensational that Carson never got to his final guests. "I never tamper with a guest when he's on a roll," he said.

Vic's roll had started almost from the moment he came on to the strains of "You've Got to Be a Football Hero" and settled himself in the chair next to Carson's desk.

Wise showman that he is, Carson realized America already knew about Vic's age, background, and fantastic kicking exploits. He chose, instead, to lead Vic into the other aspects of his life and the uncanny memory that had so intrigued Carson.

"We have a 'first' here tonight," Carson said. "Vic Waller is the first guest we're *not* going to show a film clip on. I'm sure everyone in America has seen his Fantastic Finish for the Dallas Cowboys." Turning to Vic, he said, "What I want to talk to you about is your nonsporting life, the stuff in *Sports Illustrated* that fascinated me so much."

"Oh, yeah," Vic said. "That was a fine article, written by an old pal, Dan Jenkins."

"Dan is a funny fellow. We've had him on this show before. You two grew up together, back in Fort Worth?"

"Yeah. He was the rich one."

"Rich?" said Carson.

"How rich was he?" chorused the boys in the band.

"One Christmas I ran over to his house and said, 'Dan! Dan! I got a bicycle!' He said, 'I got a car.' "

Carson and the audience broke into laughter. "Fade out, fade in," Vic said. "A couple of years ago I was at a tailgate party before a TCU football game and I met Marty Jenkins, Dan's son, who was down from New York to attend TCU. I found out we were both interested in collecting old movies on videotape. I was a little proud that I had just ponied up for a second VCR so I could rent the movies for $1.50 and then record my own copies for keepers. I told Marty, 'I have two VCRs.' And Marty said, 'We've got a dish.' "

When the laughter subsided Vic said, "Remember the Little Orphan Annie Decoder Badges?"

"Sure," Carson said. "After all, we're about the same age."

"Well . . . you're older," Vic said.

The director cut to a Carson close-up on the laughter, and Carson obliged him with his "little boy" hurt stare.

"Anyway," Vic went on, "Dan was the first one, naturally, to send in ten cents in coin and the seal from a tin of Ovaltine—or a reasonable facsimile, which none of us knew what that meant—to get the brand-new 1939 Decoder. He grandly gave me his old 1938 Decoder. So there I sat by my radio one afternoon in 1939, pencil poised, waiting for announcer Pierre Andre to give out Annie's secret code numbers for her message of the day. Andre is giving out the numbers—'seventeen . . . five . . . twenty-four'—and every kid on the block is jotting furiously and turning the dial on their decoders. Everyone would then run outside to tell everyone else that Annie's message for tomorrow was 'Danger Ahead for Daddy Warbucks.' But my pitiful little message, decoded with the 1938 Decoder, read 'Sjikst Fibty Ilb Suffo Grhcortz.' "

"Now, that is *funny!*" Carson said, laughing. "Pierre Andre. I haven't thought of him in years. Do you remember the theme song?"

Vic sang:

> *"Who's that little chatterbox?*
> *The one with curly auburn locks,*
> *Who do you see?*
> *It's Little Orphan Annie."*

Carson was wiping his eyes. "Great. Do you remember *Jack Armstrong the All-American Boy?*"

Without a pause, Vic sang:

> *"Wave the flag for Hudson High, boys,*
> *Show them how we stand,*
> *Ever shall our team be champions,*
> *Known throughout the land."*

"How do you *do* that?" Carson exclaimed.

"I don't know, it just comes." Vic shrugged. "Like, 'And it shall be my duty as District Attorney not only to prosecute to the limit of the law all persons accused of crimes perpetrated within this county, but to defend with equal vigor the rights and privileges of all its citizens!' "

"*Mr. District Attorney*, starring Jay Jostyn in the title role," Carson said gleefully.

"With Len Doyle as Harrington and Vicki Vola as Miss Miller," Vic responded.

"How about *I Love a Mystery*, with Jack, Doc, and Reggie?"

"Jack Packard, Doc Long, and Reggie York."

"That's no *fair*! You remember *last* names!"

"Vic, Sade, and Rush Gook. But I can't remember Uncle Fletcher's last name."

"Where did they live?" Carson challenged.

"At the small house halfway up in the next block."

"Where did Fibber McGee and Molly live?"

"At 79 Wistful Vista."

"What's your own address?"

"I don't know. It's some dorm at Cal Lutheran College."

That brought down the house, and Carson reluctantly broke for commercials. Each of the several times he took the breaks he chatted with Vic off-camera and became more and more convinced that he would never get to his next guests that night.

"I guess your remarkable memory serves you well in football," Carson said to him when they came back after one break.

"To use a Tom Landry expression, 'No, not really.' " Vic grinned. "All I have to remember is to take three steps."

"Are you afraid of getting hurt playing out there with all those three-hundred-pound 'kids'?"

"No, not really." He grinned again. "The only team I'm afraid of is the Cowboys. They jump on you when they're happy."

"Here you are with a new career at the age of fifty-two. Did you ever think about still another one in show business? You're good."

"No, not really," Vic said, liking the new Tom Landry game he was playing. "There are several things I could never be because I can't pretend to be something I'm not."

"Like what?"

"Like being a contestant on *Family Feud*. I could never say 'Good answer!' when it's an idiotic answer. Richard Dawson will say 'Name a household appliance that you leave plugged in all the time.' The guy will answer 'A vacuum cleaner,' and all of the other idiots will say 'Good answer! Good answer!' "

"Nothing but the truth, eh?"

"I couldn't be a TV anchorman or a weatherman because I can't laugh unless something is funny."

"As in . . . ?"

"As in, 'Well, Chip (chuckle), do you think I (guffaw) got any rain (wheeze, gasp) out at my place tonight?' And Chip laughs, 'No, Michael (giggle), but I'll bet Alice (cackle) got some out at her house.' And Alice collapses in laughter over the desk as she says, 'We'll be right back to find out.' "

"Anything else?" Carson laughed. "And please note that my laughter is genuine."

"I couldn't be a Top 40 disk jockey," Vic said seriously.

"Why not?"

"My name's not Randy."

Once when they came back Vic opened up by saying he still had a huge collection of the old Big Little Books.

"I remember Big Little Books," Carson said, drumming his pencil on the desk. "They were those stubby little books about Dick Tracy, Mickey Mouse, and Popeye with the cartoons on one page and reading on the other page. Sold for a dime back in the 1930s and 1940s. Where do you keep them?"

"I had special shelves built for them, and there they sit in yellowing splendor."

"Do you ever get them out and read them?"

"Never. I'm afraid somebody will phone to ask what I'm doing and I'll have to say I'm reading *Flash Gordon in the Water World of Mongo.*"

"You are bringing back a lot of memories," Carson said. "What do you remember most about 'yesterday'?"

"*The Saturday Evening Post* sold for a nickel. A new magazine called *Life* showed its class by charging a dime."

"How about Ma Perkins?"

"Oxydol's Own Ma Perkins. She and Shuffle Shober ran the lumberyard at Rushville Center."

"Right. What lodge did Vic belong to on *Vic and Sade*?"

"The Sacred Stars of the Milky Way."

"What was the garbageman's name on that show?"

"Mr. Gumpox. His horse was named Howard."

"What *don't* you remember?" Carson asked in amazement.

"What I had for breakfast this morning," Vic answered.

Another time when they came back Carson asked Vic, "Did you ever get to New York as a kid and get to see any of those network shows?"

"Never," Vic said. "But the first time I ever got there as a grown man, I kept looking around for the little theater off Times Square, hoping to see that doorman showing Mr. First-Nighter inside to see Barbara Luddy, Les Tremayne, or, maybe, Olan Soule."

"Olan Soule! Now there's another name out of the past," Carson exclaimed.

"I kept thinking that, surely, I'd find a glamorous night spot where Thomas L. Thomas would be singing to those zebra-striped cushions."

And Vic sang:

> *"Jump on the Manhattan Merry-Go-Round*
> *We're touring alluring old New York town,*
> *Broadway or Harlem, the musical show,*
> *Be our guest as you rest at your radio."*

The band joined in, playing the last verse with Vic:

> *"We're serving music, songs and laughter,*
> *A happy heart will follow after,*
> *And we'd like to have you all with us*
> *On the Manhattan Merry-Go-Round."*

The audience was going crazy with applause. Vic plowed on, without waiting for Carson to ask him anything.

"One afternoon I was mistaken for a New York native," Vic said, "and a lady approached me and asked, 'Can you tell me how to get to Grand Central Station from here?' I had been waiting all my life for someone to ask that.

" 'Madam,' I told her, 'as a bullet seeks its target, shining rails in every part of our great country are aimed at Grand Central Station, heart of the nation's greatest city. Drawn by the magnetic force of the fantastic metropolis, day and night great trains rush toward the Hudson River, sweep down its eastern bank for one hundred and forty miles, flash briefly past the long red row of tenement houses south of 125th Street, dive with a roar into the two-and-one-half-mile tunnel that burrows beneath the glitter and swank of Park Avenue . . . and then . . . GRAND CENTRAL STATION . . . crossroads of a million private lives, gigantic stage on which are played a thousand dramas daily!' "

Carson was convulsed with laughter, leaning back in his chair and throwing his pencil in the air. "What did the woman do?" he asked.

"Now she *knew* I was a native New Yorker. A street nut. She flashed me what I believe the newspapers would call an obscene gesture and hailed a cab."

"Do you do this for old TV shows too?" Carson asked.

"No. I do radio trivia. TV is current events. I grew up on network radio, just like you. When you do the 'Mighty Carson Art Players,' I know who the takeoff is on."

"The master—Fred Allen."

"It's Town Hall Tonight. With Portland Hoffa and Peter Van Steeden and the Ipana Troubadours."

"Ipana for the smile of beauty, Sal Hepatica for the smile of health," Carson recalled.

"I was thirty-five years old before I found out Sal Hepatica was a laxative," Vic said.

After the laugh Vic switched to a high-pitched Portland Hoffa voice and said, "Mr. Allen, did you know that when Jack Benny impersonates you, he holds his nose?" Then he switched to the nasal whine of Fred Allen, saying, "Portland, when Jack Benny impersonates me *everybody* holds his nose."

"You do the *voices* too?" Carson marveled.

"I don't do Jack Benny," Vic said. "He's yours."

"That's right. Don't forget who the star is here."

Vic responded with: "Howdoyoudo, ladies and gentlemen, this is Bob, Fort Bragg, Hope, telling you, 'Brush your teeth with Pepsodent like the old professor, and at night you won't have to put them on the dresser.' Yes, *sir*! But I wanna tell you . . ."

"That's great," Carson said.

Vic started doing the staccato beeps of a telegraph key and, in the distinctive voice of Walter Winchell, began chanting, "Good evening, Mr. and Mrs. North and South America, and all the ships at sea, let's go to press. FLASH! Dunkirk—The ragged, but valiant, remnants of the British Army have been safely evacuated back over the Channel by a fleet of British fishing boats and anything that floats. This means they will live, to fight again another day! And how, Mr. Hitler, do you like . . . those . . . apples!"

"Fantastic," Carson said. "As Edward R. Murrow said: *I Can Hear It Now*."

To which Vic, in a whiny, scratchy voice, said, "We hold the distinction of being the only nation in the history of the world that went to the poorhouse in an automobile." And then quickly, switching to the stern, tense tones of Edward R. Murrow: "That was the voice of Will Rogers, trying to teach America how to laugh its way through a Depression. . . . Franklin D. Roosevelt stood beside Chief Justice Hughes on the steps of the Capitol that raw afternoon of March fourth, and a nation with fifteen million unemployed listened . . ."

As F.D.R., Vic pitched in with "For first of all, let me assert my firm belief that the only thing we have to fear is fear itself . . . nameless, unreasoning, unjustified terror which paralyzes needed effort to convert retreat into advance."

Carson had to cut to commercials on the applause. When they came back he said, "Maybe the most famous segment of that 'I Can Hear It Now' album is the crash of the Hindenburg."

Vic became Murrow again: "It was drizzling that April night at Lakehurst, as announcer Herb Morrison stood beside a WLS sound truck to describe the arrival of the dirigible Hindenburg . . ."

Quickly into the calm voice of Morrison: "The ship is gliding majestically toward us like some great feather. These giant American Airlines flagships are waiting here to flash them to all points in the United States when they get the ship moored. It's practically standing still now; they've dropped ropes out of the nose of the ship. The back motors of the ship are just holding it, just enough—IT BURST INTO FLAME!—Get this started, get this started!

It's crashing! This is terrible! Oh, my, get out of the way, please! It's falling on the mooring mast. It's one of the worst catastrophes in the world! The flames are four or five hundred feet in the sky! It's a terrific crash, ladies and gentlemen. The smoke and the flames . . . and the frame is crashing to the ground, not quite to the mooring mast. Oh, the humanity, and all the passengers . . ."

The audience, awed for an instant, started to break into applause, but Vic began making a strange scratching noise in his throat.

"What's *that*?" Carson asked.

"Needle running out on the end of the 78 r.p.m. record," Vic explained.

"That's dynamite!" Carson laughed.

"Of course the Hindenburg crashed May 6, 1937. Murrow says 'April' on the record. I leave it in."

"Oh, hell, yes," Carson deadpanned to the camera. "Everybody knows it was May 6. I caught that immediately."

Vic was already going again: "Seven P.M., Eastern War Time, Bob Trout reporting—The Japanese have accepted our terms FULLY! That's the word we have just received from the White House in Washington. This, ladies and gentlemen, is the end of the Second World War! The United Nations, on land, on the sea, in the air, and to the four corners of the earth, are united and are victorious! We got that information on a special line from the White House, and now it's beginning to come in on the wire services too. President Truman announced it at 7 P.M., just a minute ago, and now, a Flash: MacArthur Appointed Jap Boss Over the Emperor of Japan."

After prolonged applause, Carson said to Vic, "You are really something else. That's my era, the thirties and the forties. But you've hit something with *all* of these people out there, and I'd guess a majority of them are in their twenties and thirties."

"It was a good time to be a kid," Vic said thoughtfully.

"It *was!*" Carson agreed. "You know, they were hard times, but the important thing was that we didn't *know* they were hard at the time."

Vic let that soak in and then said, "Did you ever go back to the steep hills of childhood and discover they were just gentle slopes?"

Carson nodded his head, and a smattering of applause began to slowly grow. "That's almost profound," he told Vic. "In fact, it *is* profound."

The piano began the play-off music in the background. "I can't believe it's gone this fast," he told Vic. "Listen, will you come back again? I mean it. I'd love to get you on with Dan Jenkins."

"Sure," said Vic, "as long as it's after training camp. I'm old enough to remember when *One Man's Family* was called *A Date With Judy*, but Tom Landry won't usually let me out at night."

Once the Cowboys' regular season started September 13 on *Monday Night Football*, it did, indeed, take Vic Waller a little time to break Tom Dempsey's record for the longest field goal.

Roughly, two minutes.

The game against Pittsburgh in Texas Stadium was less than 120 seconds old when Vic kicked a ninety-two-yard field goal that bested his eighty-three-yarder in exhibition play, forever welded his name in the NFL record book, and sent a sellout crowd and a national TV audience into delirium.

Howard Cosell was ecstatic.

"I tell you, gentlemen," he said to Frank Gifford and Don Meredith over the thundering din, "we are witnessing history. This can be the rejuvenation of football, and all by a man who never really played the game and is really too old to be playing it now. Yet, he is doing it. Positively amazing."

Gifford said over the crowd noise, "My only surprise is that Tom Landry opted to use Waller this early."

Meredith said, "I'm not surprised. Every game starts counting now. Tom wants to get back to the Super Bowl."

"Precisely," Cosell said. "It's like a lion marking off his turf, saying early—at the outset—that this is mine, this is what I can do, and this is what I intend to do. Intimidation, gentlemen. I assure you it will shake the Steelers for the rest of this game."

"You tell 'em, H'ard," Dandy Don said.

"No, I'm not the one telling it. I had dinner last night with Victor Francis Waller—an extremely charming and intelligent gentleman—and he intimated as much to me. He suggested this might be Landry's game plan."

"Well, H'ard, that'll be a refreshing change," Meredith said laconically. "We won't hear coaches saying anymore 'We've got to first establish our running game.' Now they'll be first establishing their kicking game."

Actually, Tom Landry hadn't planned to use Vic that early. But the way things went in the first series, and because all league games were important now, and because a national audience—that would later prove to have the highest ratings in *Monday Night Football* history—was watching, he came to another of his un-Landry-like decisions after the first three downs.

The Cowboys had elected to receive the opening kick-off, which was run back to the twenty. Dorsett made six yards on two running plays, and then a Danny White pass to Drew Pearson fell incomplete. Landry then called for the field goal that was nationwide headlines the next morning.

The ball was retrieved and, like the one in the Buffalo exhibition game, went to the Pro Football Hall of Fame in Canton, Ohio.

As it turned out, Landry used Waller only one more time that night, for a fifty-four-yard field goal that the newspapers called "a yawner." Terry Bradshaw had a hot night, throwing for three Steeler touchdowns. But so did Danny White, also throwing for three. The Cowboys won 27–21.

Dallas was 1–0 on the season.

But, then again, so were thirteen other teams that had played on Sunday.

* * *

Vic's life-style, of course, had changed.

After the team had returned from Thousand Oaks he had taken a furnished apartment in North Dallas near the Cowboys' practice field.

His daily schedule was a regimented one. On Mondays, the team had light workouts, and in the afternoon he and Rafael Septien were jogging partners. Tuesdays were a day off for the entire team.

Wednesdays there were 10 A.M. team meetings, plus the watching of films. At 3 P.M., Vic and Septien worked with the center and the holder. Then they would go with the linebackers for calisthenics.

There was the same morning schedule on Thursdays. In the afternoon Vic and Septien would drive with Ben Agajanian to Texas Stadium, where they would kick off of the artificial turf. At 5 P.M., back at the practice field, there were drills with the team on field-goal protection and field-goal rush.

Friday was devoted to kickoff returns, with both kickers practicing, and onside kick drills, with only Septien participating. Landry also put in a fake field-goal play designed exclusively for Septien in which Hogeboom would rise up to pass and Septien would drift unnoticed into the end zone to catch it. It was a beautiful little bit of deception, but the play was destined never to be used during the season.

Saturday schedules depended upon whether the Cowboys were playing at home or away on Sunday. If at home, the two kickers and the team did walk-through drills on field-goal protection. If they were to play on the road, it was the travel day on the team's chartered jet.

Two weeks into the season Ben Agajanian flew back home to California. He would be called back for brushups if his two kickers developed problems and needed him.

Fat chance.

* * *

The Cowboys' second regular season game at St. Louis was against a division foe, where wins were doubly important. So Landry made another decision.

If the Cowboys failed to make a first down on a drive, Vic was always called upon instead of the punter. He never missed and, in fact, kicked six in a row, sprinkled around two Dallas touchdowns.

Final score: Cowboys 32, Cardinals 10.

It was an old gag, of course, but previously it had been about teams so inept they had to punt after every third down.

Now Johnny Carson was saying it was the Dallas Cowboys who were using the new Rumba Offense—"One-two-three-kick."

Madison Avenue was quick to pick up on the Vic Waller craze, and now he was everywhere on TV in commercials.

He was seen plugging McDonald's, selling Coca-Cola, and asking "Do you know me?" on American Express commercials.

One young adman at a think tank meeting for the American Express people voted against using Vic in that particular commercial, saying the celebrated gimmick was negated in Waller's case because by now everyone did, indeed, know him.

Wiser heads prevailed and he was shouted down.

Vic had the national headlines stolen from him by Tony Dorsett the next week on the road against the Minnesota Vikings.

With the Cowboys backed up on their own one-yard line in the indoor Metrodome, Dallas backfield coach Al Lavan sent in a play from the bench that called for Ron

Springs to merely punch the ball straight ahead in order to get the team into better punting position. (Some wags suggested the Cowboys were just trying to get into field-goal position.)

Springs and Dorsett were to line up in the "I" formation. But Springs had left the field and was a spectator on the sidelines, thinking the Cowboys were going to use their Jayhawk formation for the run inside right tackle. In the Jayhawk, named for Jay Saldi, who was the original tight end in the formation, and Tony (Hawk) Dorsett, Dallas lines up with two wide receivers, two tight ends, and a lone running back—Dorsett.

And that's exactly what Dallas had in the backfield when Springs left the field—a lone running back. And only ten men on the field.

When Danny White turned around to hand off to Springs, he was startled to see there was only Dorsett to carry it.

The Vikings, in a 4–3 defense and seeing Dorsett as the lone running back, anticipated a slant play to the outside and did not "pinch" their defensive tackles to cut off the inside run.

The Vikings' left tackle looped to the outside. Tom Rafferty, the Dallas center, blocked the other defensive tackle, and Herb Scott, the Cowboy left guard, looped around Rafferty to take care of the middle linebacker. A Viking cornerback, who looked like he was going to make the tackle, misjudged Dorsett's speed and Dorsett blew right past him.

Tony Dorsett raced down the sidelines ninety-nine yards for a record touchdown from scrimmage that would never be bettered in the National Football League. Because NFL records are not kept in fractions, the run might be equaled someday but it would never be broken. Even if records were kept in fractions, Dorsett's feat would be near-impossible to beat since the ball was only a few inches from the goal line.

Dorsett said later that the run was ninety-nine yards, two feet and eight inches.

Ron Springs said later that if he had been the one who got the ball, he would have run out of oxygen on the long day's journey into the end zone.

Because they weren't playing at home, there was no Cowboy equipment manager to save the ball, which was lost forever in the mass excitement. Instead, Dorsett's shoes were sent to the Pro Football Hall of Fame.

Dorsett's run was a stunning achievement, made even more remarkable because it was a busted play, with not enough men on the field and the wrong man carrying the ball.

Yet, it was Vic Waller who won the game, 34–28, on field goals of fifty-one and sixty-two yards.

When Andy Freeman, Vic's longtime associate in the insurance agency, took over the business in Vic's absence, he saw himself just in the role of a caretaker while the owner was on an extended vacation.

He hadn't foreseen the impact of running a business with the name of Victor Waller on it.

Vic called Andy to see how things were going.

"You won't believe it," Freeman told him. "It's out of the roof! We've written just under one million in new policies, and it's all come in over the transom. You name it—life, auto, fire, household, mortgage changes. We even got one flood policy!"

Vic was staggered at the figures. And at the flood insurance policy. "No one buys flood," he said. "It's too expensive."

"This guy did," Andy said. "There's just one thing— they all want to meet you, to have you personally service the accounts."

"What do you tell them?"

"That you'll personally call them or see them once football season is over. But until then they'll have to deal with me or our other people."

"You're worth more money."

"Then give it to me."

"I will."

"I accept with humility and dignity."

On October 3 the Cowboys met their hated rivals, the Washington Redskins, in Texas Stadium.

The Redskins were the team to beat for the division title, this year as most years, so it was the same song, same verse for Tom Landry and Vic Waller.

Landry ordered in Waller to kick field goals on virtually every fourth down. Vic kicked seven of them as the Cowboys won a big one, 35–17.

Several newspapers noted the next day that a strange thing was now happening.

On more than one occasion the official was seen raising his arms to denote three more points *before* the ball actually went through the uprights.

An expected gulf of coolness went up between Vic and Rafael Septien, a situation that wasn't helped when they were designated as roommates on road trips and at the hotel where the Cowboys spent the night before home games.

Septien was normally a taciturn person anyway, but now he never even acknowledged Vic's presence in the room, on the bench, or at practice.

Vic liked Septien, as he did everyone on the team, but really hadn't wanted to room with him because Septien objected to smokers being around him. Vic soon learned that was no problem because they were rarely in the room except to sleep at night.

But he worried about the noncommunication. He would engage Septien in conversations that required responses.

"I'm sorry about the way things turned out," he told the younger man one night as they sat on the edges of their beds. "But I hope I'm still your friend."

"How would you feel, just kicking extra points?" Septien asked sullenly.

"I'd feel I was still contributing, and be proud that they thought enough of me to carry two kickers on the roster. Someday, years from now, somebody else might eventually beat you out if I hadn't come along. And you'd be traded."

"That's what I want. To be traded."

"But don't you see? They *aren't* trading you. Since I'm the guy, they're keeping you."

"What you mean?"

"I mean it's obvious that they—and I—don't know how long I'll last. Anytime, I could start missing. Go into a slump."

Septien snorted. "Listen, you may kick better than I do, but all you know is the insurance business. I know kicking better than you."

"And . . . ?"

"You never miss. You never will. I know."

"That shouldn't be a reason for not liking me . . . personally."

Septien, who had been talking with his head down, suddenly brought his handsome face up to look at Vic. "It's me I don't like," he said. "I keep hoping something will happen to you. That is not proper thoughts for a Christian."

The Cowboys remained undefeated through five games by beating another division foe, the Philadelphia Eagles, 30–14 in Texas Stadium.

Vic's three field goals were "gimmies" of forty, thirty-seven, and forty-three yards.

A league memo to officials had stopped the nervous trait of premature signaling that his kicks were good before they went through, but now the newspapers and TV noted another innovation in the game when Vic Waller was playing. It started at Texas Stadium, but it was picked up by all of the Cowboys' opponents on the road.

Stadiums were raising the net behind the goalposts on his *kickoffs* as well as his field goals.

Footballs were expensive.

The violent world of pro football came home, most vividly, to Victor Waller, former armchair quarterback, on October 17, when, under a gray and lowering sky, the Cowboys defeated the Browns before a booing crowd in Cleveland, 44–27.

He wasn't hit, but he was shocked, stunned, and humiliated.

He had become accustomed to the taunts of the opposing teams, the jeers, the murderous looks on their faces as they rushed him. But now he came up against the most hopeless emotion of them all—total frustration.

Vic was called upon to kick a forty-four-yarder. It was, of course, good.

The huge defensive end of the Browns shuddered to a stop in front of Vic after the kick, his black face contorted and covered with beads of sweat.

"Muthahfuckah!" he shouted. He spat in Vic's face.

Vic reeled away. Nothing like that had ever happened to him in his life. The ebony giant stalked him. "You takin' my livin' away!" he screamed.

The referee, standing beside them, was incensed. He furiously hurled his flag at the defensive end's feet. "That'll cost you fifteen on the kickoff," he yelled.

The giant looked down at the referee, all his frustration of a long, long afternoon pouring out. "So what, man?" he demanded. "It goin' out of the end zone, anyway. What diff'rence do it make?"

The referee picked up his flag and started back down the field. And as he trotted in a fine mist that was beginning to fall, he thought to himself, "The man's right. Absolutely right. What difference does it make?"

CHAPTER

9

Since his first exploits in the Buffalo game on national TV, and his appearance on *The Tonight Show,* more than a thousand letters had poured into Cowboy headquarters for Vic.

He managed to glance through them all, but knew he could never answer all of them. They came from everywhere in the nation, from men and women and children who wanted only to praise him, to communicate with him, to ask for autographs and pictures. The ultimate outpouring of fans to a hero.

Between games he was in constant demand for interviews and appearances on TV sports shows. And it was at Verne Lundquist's Tuesday-night sportscast of WFAA–Channel 8 in Dallas that he met her.

"Hi, I'm Ellen Wade, the assistant P.R. at the station," she said, extending her hand. "I'm your tour guide tonight. I'll take you back to Verne."

She had been waiting in the lobby, at the door. Beautiful. Shoulder-length brown hair with bangs. Eyes that might be brown except for just a touch of blue, lips with just a touch of lipstick. Fashionably dressed, knockout figure. Maybe twenty-one, or twenty-three, tops. And no ring on her left hand. Vic wondered why he had immediately looked for a ring.

He went back to the studio with her, sometimes falling behind a step or two and wondering why he was so anxious to watch her hips as she walked. And wondering why he had this desire to smell her hair.

During the interview Vic found himself looking beyond the lights just to catch glimpses of her in the background. And when it was over, and all the good-byes had been said to Lundquist and his crew, he found himself elated that she had waited to accompany him to the door.

If she hadn't asked him, he knew he would have asked her.

"Can I buy you a drink on my expense account?" she said.

"I'd like that very much," he said.

"The name's Ellen Wade, in case you don't remember."

"The problem isn't remembering you," he said. "The problem is trying to forget you."

She stopped. Looking at him, smiling at what he said. When they went through the door, he smelled her hair.

They went to the Antares restaurant, the glittering global spire high atop Reunion Tower, where the room slowly revolved around the lighted skyscrapers of Dallas.

"I have a confession to make," Ellen said after their drinks came. "I wasn't assigned to meet you tonight. I told my boss I wanted to do it."

"You like football?" Vic asked.

"I loathe it," Ellen said. "It's a dip-shit game. I haven't been to a game since college, and I've never watched a Cowboy game on TV. I've never seen you play."

"You're not a football groupie, then?" Vic laughed.

"No, I just wanted to meet you."

"Why?"

"I've just wanted to, ever since I saw you on 'Johnny Carson.' You said a lot of things that kinda got to me. I thought you'd be a nice person to know."

"What did I say that got to you?"

She sipped at a glass of white wine. "Mainly, it was when you said that thing about the steep hills of childhood just being gentle slopes when you go back home. I really like that. I knew what you meant."

The room had revolved to where they could see the distant lights of Fort Worth's skyline, thirty-two miles away.

"We have the same hometown," she said, pointing west.

"You from Fort Worth? Where did you go to high school?"

"Southwest," she answered.

Vic laughed. "Southwest wasn't even built when I went to Paschal. When did you graduate?"

"In '73," she said.

Vic drank his martini as he did some mental arithmetic. "That makes you twenty-seven, right?"

"Right. I was a 1955 baby."

"I was a 1930 baby," Vic said.

"I know. I know all about you. I never do read *Sports Illustrated*, but after I saw you on the Carson show I went all the way to the library to read Dan Jenkins's article on you. I love his books, even though I don't like sports. I especially loved what he wrote about you."

"Well, I guess there's no way around it. No two ways about it," Vic said in mock sadness.

"What do you mean?" she smiled.

Vic sighed. "Well, I was twenty-five years old when you were born. You're sitting here in a romantic room having a drink with a man who's old enough to be your father."

"I never think of things like that," Ellen said. "After you pass a certain age there's really no difference in people's ages. I mean, at twenty-seven I'm not exactly going to say I have to get my rest because I've got a jacks tournament in the morning."

Vic laughed. "How did someone as lovely as you get to be twenty-seven and not be married?" He pointed to her ring finger on her left hand.

"I think the standard answer is that the right man never came along," she said. "I lived with a guy once when I was at the University of Texas, but when he wanted to get married, I realized that I suddenly didn't."

"Why?"

"Oh, neither of us wanted any children, just careers. We were both journalism majors down at Texas. I got my degree, and he eventually dropped out. After a couple of years I realized I *was* raising a child—him. I decided if I ever got married it would be to someone who knew what he wanted to be when he grew up."

"What's he doing now?"

She laughed. "You'll never believe it. It's another thing you said on the Carson show that made me sit up and take notice. Remember when you said you could never be a disk jockey because your name wasn't Randy? Well, he's a disk jockey, in Idaho, last time I heard—and his name is Randy."

Vic ordered another martini. Ellen said she could nurse her wine until this time next week.

"Well, you know everything about me," Vic said. "Tell me more about yourself."

"Born in Nashville. Moved to Fort Worth when my father was transferred there when I was two. Went to Southwest, used to see your name on your insurance office, lost my virginity at the University of Texas, lost my father to cancer, and my mother went back to Nashville to live with relatives. Worked for a while as a reporter in Kansas City, and came back here when Channel Eight liked my résumé. Don't smoke, don't drink, love to go to New York and see Broadway shows, and I'm a frustrated writer. I keep sending off free-lance articles and getting rejection slips."

"Where do you live?"

"I took an apartment over here a couple of years ago. I go back to Fort Worth every now and then to see girlfriends."

"How about boyfriends?"

"One or two over here. Nothing serious."

The pianist at the piano-bar was singing a Perry Como love song called "I Think of You." Vic found himself looking into Ellen's eyes across the candlelit table. Touch of blue, but they sometimes looked brown.

Neither said a word for a while as the lyrics of "I Think of You" softly filled the room.

"I'm drowning," Vic said.

He didn't have to explain it to her. "I think I am too," she said.

"I think we just found 'our song,' " Vic said.

They talked for an hour. Then Vic paid the tab, helped Ellen into her coat, and they took the elevator down to the street. He held her hand as he walked her to her car.

"This one is mine," she said. "The white Thunderbird. Can I drive you to your car?"

"No, I'm just around the corner. I'd like to call you. Are you in the book?"

"Yes."

He put his hands on her shoulders, wanting to kiss her. But he didn't. Instead, he took Ellen's face in his hands and asked her, "Do your eyes bother you?"

"No. Why do you ask?"

"Because they bother me," he said.

He spent Wednesday sitting through a lot of green lights, until somebody behind him would honk. All he could think of was Ellen Wade.

He phoned her that night and they talked for an hour, like teenagers. Vic asked if he could take her out to dinner Thursday night.

They went to a quiet restaurant in North Dallas. They lingered over an after-dinner drink until Vic looked at her and said:

"Listen, and don't say anything . . . I'm not very good at this. It's been a long time. . . . I know it's totally crazy to think I could say this after so short a time. But I love you. . . . That's a phrase a lot of people throw around loosely, but I don't."

She waited a minute, and then said softly, "I know it's crazy. I don't throw that phrase around loosely, either. But I love you too."

"I've known that I loved you since the first time I saw you," Vic said.

"I think I knew I loved you ever since the first time I saw you too. But the first time I saw you, you were a thousand miles away on television. Vic, can it really happen this fast?"

"Not even in bad movies," he answered. "I haven't even kissed you."

Without a word they got up and drove to Vic's apartment.

Inside the door, he kissed her long and tenderly. "I want to kiss you all over," he whispered.

He put on the Perry Como single of "I Think of You" that he had purchased that day and set the stereo where the record would keep playing over and over.

He undressed her in the bedroom. Her body, illuminated by the dim living-room lamplight filtering down the hallway, was beautiful and perfect. He was so excited, so nervous, that he was worried he might not be able to perform. It was a needless worry. He entered her slowly, gently, lost in a love like he had never known before.

"I'm in you, Ellen," he whispered. "We're as close as two people can be."

"I love you," she whispered back, her eyes closed. "Forever and always."

Afterward, she lay in his arms and they talked for another hour.

"Spend the night?" Vic asked.

"I won't sleep," she said.

"Go to sleep, little girl. I just want you to know that wherever you are, whatever you're doing, whatever time it is, whatever day it is, you'll know that there's someone loving you."

" 'Little girl,' " she repeated, closing her eyes and savoring his words.

"My little girl," he corrected.

They made love again that night, and a third time when they awoke to pale light coming through the bedroom blinds.

On Sunday the Dallas Cowboys, again employing their "Rumba Offense" with Vic kicking four field goals, defeated the New York Giants 26–10 in the Meadowlands. They were now 7–0 on the season, and the only undefeated team in either conference.

Vic phoned her from LaGuardia.

"You 'dun good' today," Ellen told him.

"You watched the game?"

"It's still a dip-shit game, but there's no way I'm not going to see you whenever I can. I hated it today. Watching you on TV and yet knowing you were twelve hundred miles away."

"Miles can never separate us," he said. "Just lie between us."

She was touched. "Oh, Vic, hurry home."

"I'm coming, Ellen, I'm coming."

CHAPTER

....

10

They were together constantly. On Sundays, Ellen not only watched the out-of-town Cowboy games on TV, but she began to attend the home games in Texas Stadium, sitting with the Cowboy wives and girlfriends. If Vic felt an age gap with his teammates on the field, Ellen was right at home with her new women friends in the stands.

To Vic that fall of 1982 would always mean to him the time he had fallen in love with Ellen, and the time that an adoring public and an admiring media had suddenly begun to fall out of love with him.

Some were beginning to call him a man who was ruining football.

Vic Waller, the man the nation had been clamoring to watch, was robbing the fans of the one indispensable ingredient to all sports—the question of who is going to win the game.

Crowds began diminishing at Cowboy games, both at home and on the road. Slowly, then drastically, TV ratings on Cowboy games, the highest in the league, began dropping. The grumblings began about the middle of October from cabdrivers, at office coffee breaks, in bars, and on golf courses, where men were now spending more and more Sunday afternoons.

But it went unsaid nationally until the night of November 1, when the Cowboys made their second appearance on *Monday Night Football*.

Howard Cosell was livid.

The Cowboy offense was impotent, failing to score a single touchdown in San Francisco against the 49ers, the team that had kept them out of the Super Bowl the year before. But Vic Waller had kicked a record eight field goals for a 24–14 victory.

"I tell you, gentlemen," Cosell said to Frank Gifford and Don Meredith, "I don't like what I'm seeing here tonight. This is not good for football."

"Now, H'ard," Meredith chided, "that's not what you said on the opening game when Waller kicked a ninety-two-yarder."

"I tell it like it is," Cosell said. "That's the way it was in September. This is the way it is in November."

Meredith sang, off-key, "Will you love me in November the way you loved me in September . . . ?"

"Frankly, no, Dandy. I have the constitutional right to change my mind. As have others. The network and Pete Rozelle might not want me to say it, but a fact is a fact—the crowds are way off, and every time Victor Waller kicks an automatic three points, you can almost hear the click of TV sets being turned off all over the country. Gentlemen, the suspense of the game is *gone!*"

"Now, Howard," Gifford put in diplomatically, "that's a little strong. Maybe they're waiting for him to miss."

"And maybe they're waiting for a fish to take a bath," Cosell said dourly. "Think about it. What if you had a baseball pitcher who struck out every batter he faced, every game? Why play the game? What if you had a batter who could hit every pitch out of the park? He'd bat fourth in the lineup, always be walked, and you'd never see him hit. What if you had a golfer who could score a hole in one on every swing? It would be amazing to see someone go around in eighteen, but if there was no doubt about who was going to win, why bother to watch the next time?"

Cosell sighed. "I could carry the analogy on to every sport. Basketball, track, hockey, boxing, everything. The point is—nobody pays to see who comes in second."

On November 7 the Cowboys played St. Louis at Texas Stadium, winning 37–14 with three Waller field goals.

Tom Landry was quizzed about the Cowboys' super weapon at his weekly press luncheon.

"Tom," began the Dallas *Morning News*, "how do you justify Waller's never-miss scoring with your avowed practice of never running up the score on an opponent?"

Landry was ready for the question. "Well, first, I assure you that I haven't changed my stand on that. I never have run up the score on an opponent, and I never will. I won't ever change on that. I might be stubborn, but I have a certain code that I play by. I have a feeling for the people involved in the game. I have a sensitivity toward the coaches I compete against. It is done by a few coaches in the game, but I wouldn't do it even if it became acceptable by a lot of coaches."

Landry smiled. "Now let's get to the crux of your question. If you'll think back, there has never been a game this season, including the preseason games, when I used Waller for anything but *winning* a game. He's never been used late in a game that was already won by us.

"Our offense hasn't been all that good this year in the matter of scoring touchdowns. Remember, it only takes one touchdown and an extra point by the other team to wipe out two of our field goals. By the same token, it takes three of our field goals to wipe out just one of the opponent's touchdowns and extra points."

"But," the reporter persisted, "doesn't this sort of ne-

gate all of the NFL's long-standing policies toward bringing parity to the game and opening up the game? The
kickoffs were moved back to the thirty-five so there would
be more runbacks. The goalposts were moved ten yards to
the back of the end zone to make field goals more difficult. Both of those changes are out the window with
Waller kicking. To achieve parity the league has the
weakest teams drafting first and the best teams drafting
last. Scheduling of nondivision games for each year is based
on weaker teams not having to play stronger teams in
order to obtain later parity. With Waller there's no more
parity whatever the scheduling."

"Well, all I can say to that is that the Cowboys were
fortunate to find Vic Waller." Landry grinned. "He might
have gone to any other team."

The Fort Worth *Star-Telegram* asked, "Tom, I think
maybe the thing the Cowboys are taking heat on is the
fact that Waller is kicking on every possession that the
Cowboys don't score a touchdown. No punts."

"Again," Landry said, "as long as we're not piling on
points—and we're not—I have to use any weapon I have
to score when our offense fails to generate a touchdown.
To do anything else—to punt when we have an automatic
three points available—would be betraying the game."

The Dallas *Times Herald* asked, "How does the rest of
the team feel about Waller dominating the glory? Or, if
that's a wrong choice of words, dominating the scoring?"

"I'm sure there are some receivers and running
backs who are disappointed. But I'm also sure that
they're intelligent enough to know that the situation is
entirely in their hands. They have the first shot at
scoring. Waller only comes in after they have had their
chance."

"Tom," said the Dallas *Morning News*, "the NFL's old
rule on all home games being blacked out—later changed
to all home games not being sold out to be blacked

out—was predicated on the belief that no one would come
to the stadium to see something they could watch for free
in their homes. The old phrase was that football would be
like studio wrestling. With the crowds starting to stay
away, what do you think about Texas Stadium football
being turned into studio wrestling."

"You said that. I didn't," Landry said evenly.

On November 14 the Cowboys played Tampa Bay at
Texas Stadium, winning 19–7 with four Waller field goals.

Tex Schramm had long before put a limit of 50,000 on
the number of season tickets the Cowboys would sell,
even though other successful NFL teams had a policy of
selling out their stadiums to season-ticket holders.

Schramm and owner Clint Murchison had always felt,
once the good years arrived, that 15,000 tickets per game
should be held back for over-the-counter sales to out-of-
towners and those locals who could not afford to attend
every game.

Now the crowds were dipping below 50,000, which not
only meant that the Cowboy games were blacked out locally,
and the organization was losing concession, parking, and
program moneys, but that the absent season-ticket holders
weren't able to find people to give their tickets to.

In the New York *Daily News* a letter to the editor from
a Giants fan summed it up:

"When I was a kid I read every Ellery Queen mystery I
could lay my hands on. I also had a bad habit—I would
always turn to the last page in the book to see how many
pages the book had. You couldn't help but see the last
words in the book.

"One of the Queen books, *The French Powder Mystery*,
was ruined for me because it had a gimmick. The last
words in the book were the name of the murderer! I didn't
want to read it after seeing that.

"Just like I don't care about watching Dallas Cowboy games anymore, even when they play the Giants. Or even watching other NFL games when we already know who's going to win the Stupor Bowl in January."

On November 21 the Cowboys played Washington at Washington in a pivotal game on the Redskins' turf.

John Riggins ran wild for Washington, but the Cowboys still won, 40–35, on four Waller field goals.

"We were extremely lucky to win today," Tom Landry told the media at the postgame dressing-room interviews. "I think it's obvious, by a five-point victory, that I've proved my point—a last-minute touchdown by Washington would have wiped out our winning field goals."

"Victory Vic" was no longer sought out for postgame quotes. There didn't seem to be much news in automation.

But Vic was sought out the next day back in Dallas at practice by his best friend on the team, John Dutton.

"You look kinda glum," Dutton said to him as they stood along the sidelines. "Fickle public getting to you?"

"Oh, I don't know," Vic sighed. "That's part of it, I suppose. The other part is that while the critics are yelling I'm doing too much, I don't feel like I'm doing as much as the rest of the team. Sometimes I get to feeling that I'm really not a part of this team. I don't have to work as hard as the rest of you, and I just do *one thing* and then go sit down. I don't feel I'm really a football player like all the rest of you."

"Well, if it'll make you feel any better," Dutton said, "I'm not a football player, either. Not like it was when we were kids, anyway. I just play offensive tackle. Not only that, but I just play *left* offensive tackle. That's the only plays I have, the only thing I practice, the only thing I *do*."

Dutton smiled and pointed down the sidelines. "Look at ole Jay Saldi over there. He's a tight end—*only*. But he's worse off than us. He's a tight end only on *third down* situations. None of us play football anymore, as we once knew it."

"Do you think the other players resent me?" Vic asked.

"Nope," said Dutton. "If they can score, they'll score."

"I hope you're right," Vic said. "I've been thinking about it a lot."

Actually, Vic thought to himself, that wasn't exactly correct. What he thought about—constantly—was Ellen.

CHAPTER

. . . .

11

The Thanksgiving Day game between the Cowboys and the Cincinnati Bengals was generally considered to be the dullest in NFL history. Neither team scored a touchdown, and the Cowboys fumbled away so many possessions that Waller had only four field goals. The Bengals managed only a safety, and the Cowboys stayed undefeated by the unlikely score of 12–2.

After the game Vic and Ellen drove to Fort Worth for a belated evening Thanksgiving Day dinner at the home of Andy Freeman, his insurance associate, and his wife, Daphne. Because the Cowboys would be off until Monday, they planned to spend three whole days in Fort Worth.

"I'm afraid that wasn't a very exciting game today," Vic said as they drove toward Fort Worth on I-30.

"I worry about you out there," she said. "I'm always afraid you're going to get hurt."

"So am I," he laughed. "But they give me good protection."

As the Fort Worth skyline came into view, Vic rolled down his window and impulsively yelled to the world, "I LOVE ELLEN!"

She laughed and leaned back against the seat. "I can't get over how easy and natural this all is," she said. "How you just walked into my life and immediately *fit*. It's like we've been together for years."

"I know," he said, squeezing her hand. "When we're apart I know we're really not. I breathe when you breathe."

Andy and Daphne Freeman took to Ellen right off, and she to them. "I can't tell you how nice it is of you to postpone your Thanksgiving dinner just for us," Ellen told them.

"Glad to do it," Andy said. "There's just the two of us, no kids, no in-laws. Night's just as good as day for us."

"Just so long as he gets his turkey," Daphne said.

"And my predinner holiday drinks," Andy said. "Vic, I've got some Beefeater for you, but I'm going to let you do the vermouth part. White wine for you, right, Ellen?"

They all grouped around Daphne in the kitchen, asking what they could do to "help," which was, of course, absolutely nothing. It had turned cold outside, and the kitchen windows were steamed. The room was filled with the aroma of roasting turkey and the friendly sounds of four voices going on at once.

Vic looked into Ellen's eyes as Andy and Daphne argued over the basting process. "I'm drowning," he told her. "I can't hear a word they're saying to us."

He kissed her lightly, saying, "I've never loved you as much as I do at this very moment."

They spent the night with the Freemans, and the next morning they drove off to see their hometown again. This time, together.

They went to the famed Stockyards area where the Old West still lived. To the lush Japanese Gardens. To the stunning downtown Water Gardens. Past Vic's former home and his apartment, and past the Wedgwood home Ellen had shared with her parents. To the celebrated art museums that the city was noted for. They rode the world's longest miniature train through the wooded glades of Forest Park, and, feeling like a kid, he bought her a strawberry snow cone.

Andy Freeman had given them the key to his secluded fishing cabin in the woods around Lake Worth. On Sunday they got a bucket of Kentucky Fried Chicken and a six-pack of Coors and drove to the rustic spot, peaceful in its autumn foliage.

They walked hand in hand through the woods. And they made love twice in the comfortably furnished cabin.

"You want to know how much I love you?" Vic asked as they ate chicken and gazed at one another across the painted countenance of Colonel Sanders. "Here I am on one of the rare Sundays when I can see other teams playing football, and I'm not even considering turning on that TV set over there."

They talked for hours, just as they had been talking for hours ever since the first night. "Have you noticed," he told her, "how we never run out of things to talk about? That's what I call 'fitting right in.'"

"We're so alike," she said.

"I keep wondering, where's the flaw, Ellen? You're beautiful, kind, gentle, intelligent, witty. We never have to explain what we're talking about. We never have a disagreement. You're sincere and you believe in loyalty, and you're the most genuine person I ever knew. The sex is great. We like doing the same things. So tell me, where are the flaws?"

"Oh, I've got 'em."

"Name one."

"I can't," she said brightly.

He laughed, moving across the room to straighten a curtain that had been caught on the back of a chair when they had opened it.

"That was bothering you, wasn't it?" she asked him.

"Can't help it." He shrugged. "I've always been that way. Everything has to be just right. A place for everything and everything in its place. I'm Felix Unger. The women in my office say I even have neat trash."

"You're so methodical . . . about everything. You *see* things that no one else would even think of."

"You're talking about last night, aren't you?"

"It was the only time in my life," she said, "that I've been waked up after midnight so someone could show me that the digital clock read 'one-two-three-four.' "

"But you still love me . . . ?"

"You're crazy," she laughed.

"Of course," he agreed. Then he added, "No, I'm not. You know why I'm not crazy? Because I know I'm crazy, and crazy people don't know they're crazy."

"Only my crazy Vic would come to such a logical conclusion," she said. "Now let's get on the bed before you decide to make it."

Later she went into the shower to wash her hair, and then sat cross-legged in her robe at the kitchen table, blowing her hair with her dryer.

"You might as well watch," she laughed. "This is as bad as I'll ever look."

"And you're still beautiful," he said. "I watched you sleeping last night, and when you got up this morning. I've never seen anyone look that lovely when they're sleeping or just waking up."

"How did Marsha Ann look when she dried her hair?"

"I don't know. She didn't even own a dryer. She had a permanent weekly appointment at the beauty shop for the works, from nails to lashes. She always looked great, but her hair was always like sleeping with a football helmet."

Ellen laughed. "I hate beauty shops. I like doing it myself." She turned off the dryer and said to Vic, "Did you love her?"

"Yes," he said, not being startled by the abrupt question. "But it was different. Not at all like the love I have for you. We had gone together since high school. I never

really knew anyone else. As the years go by that torrid
kind of romantic love softens into what I suppose you'd
call warm friendship."

"Could that be us someday?"

"Maybe. But I can't imagine it."

"I can't, either."

He reached over and held her hand. "I can't get
over how lucky I am to have found you. I could have
been reading gas meters in Amarillo and you could
have been a schoolteacher in San Francisco—and I
would have lived out my life never knowing there was
an Ellen."

"I know," she said softly. "But we did find each
other. Someone was looking out for us."

"How can I be so lucky that someone hasn't taken you
in all these years?"

"I wasn't looking," she said.

"I wasn't, either," he answered. "I was perfectly con-
tent to live out my life alone."

"And now . . . ?"

They had talked about everything, except this.

Vic was silent for a minute. And then he said, "I don't
know how to say this, because I've never said it before. It
was Marsha Ann who said it to me a long time ago. So I
wrote it."

He went over to his coat and handed her a folded piece
of paper.

It read, "My Ellen— I want you to marry me, and come
along with me through the years. —Your Vic."

She looked up from the note and said, "Oh, yes, my
baby, yes, yes."

She closed her eyes and shook her head. "You still
want me, with my hair looking like a wet puppy?"

"Only forever and always," he said.

"When should we think about doing it?" she asked.

"I want it to be right. For you. I want to go on a

honeymoon. A honeymoon cruise to somewhere," he said. "It would have to be after the football season."

"Start losing," she said. "No Super Bowl."

He laughed, and they kissed, and she said, "My sweet, sweet husband. I love the sound of that word."

"I'll promise you three things," he said. "I'll never lie to you, never hurt you, and I'll never bore you."

She fell into his arms, her tears wet against his cheek.

"There's one other advantage to marrying me," he said. "You won't have to change the initials on your towels."

CHAPTER

....

12

Kelso Chandler was a man who spent his fifty-six years waiting at the door of life and going through on someone else's push. Long before the term "wimp" came into being, Kelso was always "it" in any game the kids played in his Denver neighborhood. But he soon learned to earn the admiration of his peers by doing the things they had neither the ingenuity nor the nerve to perform.

It was Kelso Chandler who brought the age-old custom of mischief-making to a fine art. As a teenager he thought up the idea of getting a welding torch and solidifying cars that were parked bumper-to-bumper at high school football games. He delighted his cronies by walking through the crowded lobby of Denver's leading hotel, posing as a page and shouting loudly, "Call for Mr. Meoff . . . Mr. Meoff . . . Mr. Jack Meoff."

When a crotchety parking-lot attendant at his neighborhood theater gave him a bad time, Kelso didn't do anything as mundane as egging the man's house in revenge. He merely pulled in one night driving his father's car and began removing the hubcaps. When the armed guard accosted him in the noisy act, Kelso meekly claimed it was his own car. When the guard had him arrested anyway, Kelso pulled out the registration papers at headquarters and sued the watchman for false arrest.

Convinced that in later life he never wanted to carry anything heavier than an insurance policy, he spent days during World War II dreaming of the perfect job he wanted to have someday. His number one choice was to be the marquee changer at the theater in New York where it looked like *Oklahoma!* was going to run for five years. Number two was to be the staff photographer at *Reader's Digest*, a magazine that at the time was noted for not ever using photos. Number three was to be the man in movie musicals who did nothing but spin a newspaper in front of the camera until it suddenly stopped, right side up, to reveal a headline reading CANARY SISTERS BOFFO IN BOSTON. Number four was to be the guy who made five-star collar insignias for generals. There couldn't be too much demand for them.

When he started seeing highway signs advertising "Broken Cookies—29¢ a Bag," he toyed with the idea of being the man who broke the cookies. Somebody had to do it.

Instead, he settled for being a bail bondsman in Denver as soon as he was belatedly able to graduate from high school and persuade his father to stake him to the investment.

Haunting the corridors of the Denver city and county jails, Kelso Chandler soon became a legend with the cops and reporters. It was Chandler who went the bail one morning for a prisoner who had no arms. As Chandler bade farewell to the armless man, a reporter for the Denver *Post*, sensing a story, hurried up to Kelso to ask, "What's the deal on that guy?"

"Aw, he's just a poor ole boy who couldn't take care of himself back in the jail," Kelso said, lighting a cigar. "I decided to go his bond, though I'll probably never get it back."

"Well, gee, Kelso, that's nice of you," the reporter said. "What did they have him for?"

"He was downtown last night, and a little ole lady came up and asked him to point out the bus station," Chandler said through a cloud of smoke. "They got him on indecent exposure."

In 1950, Kelso married Betty Sue. He had been horny ever since.

When she became pregnant the doctor suggested they not have any sexual relations past the seventh month.

One night Kelso turned to Betty Sue and said, "Look, Mike is six years old. I *know* it's all right, if you'll just go back and ask the doctor."

Kelso Chandler had to get married to find out what the stone ache was. He was sitting there one night reading the paper and thought he had appendicitis. "Mike doesn't know how lucky he is," he shouted at Betty Sue. "He barely got in under the wire or he wouldn't be here today."

Kelso maintained that Betty Sue was a virgin again, because it had "growed back over."

One day Betty Sue came home and said the church was having a white elephant sale but she wasn't sure what a white elephant was. "A white elephant," Kelso explained, "is something you paid money for but no longer use or have any use for. Give 'em our box of rubbers."

When he was forty years old Kelso decided to get a vasectomy. He felt it might make things better at home if Betty Sue no longer had a fear of pregnancy. He also felt he might feel freer to get "some strange," since he wasn't getting any even vaguely familiar, anyway. Those who might have said the second reason outweighed the first would get no argument from Kelso. When he first started getting gray it was his pubic hairs he culled, not those on his head. "First place they get a close look," he said.

The operation was a painless thirty-minute session in the doctor's office. But when it was over the doctor failed to say what Kelso's vasectomy friends had told him he would say. That it takes awhile to get rid of the remaining live sperm, and that he would have to bring a specimen back in six weeks to be checked under a microscope.

"Do you want to see me again in six weeks?" Kelso asked.

"Oh, not necessarily six weeks," the doctor said. "We figure it takes about twelve times."

There was a pause as Kelso reflected. "Twelve times!" he exclaimed. "Hell, I may see you in ten years. I may be the first guy to ever get a vasectomy and not live long enough to know if it was successful."

Chandler told friends later, "I ran 'em off by hand and mailed it in."

In 1971, Chandler moved his family to another city and became a successful businessman.

Like businessmen everywhere, he got up about 8 A.M., put on his business suit, had breakfast, kissed his wife good-bye, and went to the office.

The only difference was that Kelso Chandler lived in Las Vegas, his business suit was slacks, sports shirt, sport coat, and Gucci loafers, and his office was above a downtown casino where he had quickly become the nation's number one handicapper of sporting events. Kelso Chandler set the line for the nation on NFL football.

Years ago the line had been set in New York. Now it was in Las Vegas. And when Kelso Chandler talked, the gambling nation listened.

Kelso's office was simply furnished: three desks, three telephones, three typewriters, a calculator, a computer tied into a sports information service, and two clerks. Originally the clerks had been men. Now they were women, one of whom Kelso was nailing, and the other he wasn't, mainly because of the first one's close proximity in the office.

Kelso's system was not as simple as his office surroundings. He stayed on the phone for hours with sources in all NFL cities. He had absolute confidence in their judgments, but, moreover, he had absolute confidence in his own judgment. He had access to all injury reports on the wire. He took away "points" from known fumblers, gave "points" for home-field advantage. He grew wary if too-large sums were being bet in too many places in a certain city. He had previous records, previous strengths, previous weaknesses, previous tendencies, previous turnovers firmly implanted in his computer and his computer-like memory.

Mondays were his longest days. From all this information he began shifting numbers, first in one direction, then the other, in what he called the early line. There was a limit that could be bet into the early line at half-point increments.

Tuesdays, armed with additional information, and the results of *Monday Night Football*, he produced the hard numbers for the final line, open to all bettors. And this formula was almost simplicity itself.

"I ask myself if I would bet a game at a number," Chandler said. "I keep moving the number until I feel I wouldn't bet either side. That's the number I end up with."

On December 6, the Monday after the Cowboys had defeated the New Orleans Saints 27–10 in the Superdome, Kelso calibrated Dallas for their next game.

He threw out such factors as home-field advantage or disadvantage. He threw out previous records. He threw out injury reports.

He only knew that Vic Waller, who had kicked two long-distance field goals against the Saints, Vic Waller, a man he had never met but had come to hate, wasn't on any injury report.

And then Kelso Chandler did something he had never done before in his career.

He took the Cowboys off the board.

CHAPTER

....

13

Ever since the arrival of the affluent TV years, the National Football League had enjoyed a healthy average of a 22 rating and a 36 share on its prime-time national telecasts.

With the arrival of Victor Waller as the star of America's Team, the Cowboys had shot to an incredible 38 rating and a 62 share.

Just as incredibly, the Cowboys' Thanksgiving Day game, on a day traditionally reserved for football watching, had sunk to an astonishing 7.2 rating and 13 share, 67th and dead last in the Nielsen ratings.

Sponsors began bailing out like the 101st Airborne Division on training maneuvers.

But the Cowboys weren't the only team to feel the blow. CBS reported that ratings were off in other NFC cities, although not as drastically, as apathy spread. As December got under way the feeling was in those NFC cities that their team was not going to the Super Bowl, no matter how good their won-lost record was.

Things were only slightly better in AFC cities, with NBC also showing drops in the ratings. The feeling there seemed to be that it would be interesting to see who won the championship, but after that it meant only who would come in second in the Super Bowl.

All over the league, in both conferences, team owners were worried.

On December 12, after the Cowboys had defeated Houston 19–10 in Texas Stadium on four Vic Waller field goals, the owner in one city placed a call to the owner in another city.

"Clint, this is Otis Pepper. I sure hate to bother you at home, but I've got something I just have to say to you."

Clint Murchison frowned. Otis Pepper was the last of the gentlemen. He didn't *know* how to be angry or impolite. But Murchison could tell from the cadence and uncomfortably stern tone of his opening words that Otis had something angry on his mind.

"Otis! Great to hear from you. At home or anyplace. What can I do for you?"

"Clint, I can usually control myself, but this . . . this *thing!* has just . . . has just put frost on my balls."

Now Murchison smiled. Otis Pepper also didn't know how to cuss.

"Well, what would that be, Otis?"

"You know da . . . doggone well what I'm talking about. It's this Waller fellow that you hired. Clint, he's eating my dinner. And the dinner of every owner and player in this business. That includes you also, my friend. The man is ruining football."

"Now, Otis, I wouldn't go so far as to say—"

"Well, I'd go so far as to say that," Otis said, beginning to sputter a bit. "I've come to hate the man's very name."

Murchison waited for his caller to calm down.

"He's costing every owner in the league a bundle," Otis continued. "Crowds are down everywhere. Ticket sales, parking, concessions, programs. The TV ratings don't matter right now, but they will the next time Pete Rozelle goes in to negotiate contracts with the networks."

Again, Murchison just waited, saying nothing.

Otis Pepper sighed. "Shoot, I can afford to lose the money—although some of the owners can't—but that's not the point. It's not the money. This guy's ruining the game of football. And I love football. That's why I'm in the game. And, Clint, I know that's why you're in the game."

"Yes, I know that too. But what would you have me do about it, Otis?"

"Put him on waivers!" Pepper blurted out. "I'll guarantee you that not a single team would pick him up. I can promise you that, Clint. Word of honor from some old friends. Gentleman's agreement."

"Otis," Murchison said with a touch of weariness, "you know that Tom and Tex would never let me do that."

"Bull . . . corn! You're the owner. They'd do anything you told them they had to do."

"Well, then, look at it this way, Otis. Suppose that I did. You wouldn't pick him up, but you know you can't speak for all the other owners. Somebody would pick him up."

"No! I'll guarantee you!" Otis was pleading. "They'd all agree. Give one of them a sure winner, like Waller, and that team, and the entire league, would be right in the same boat the Cowboys are in right now. The *game* would still be ruined. The results would still be the same. They don't *want* Waller! They just want him out of the business."

Clint reflected, running a hand across his crew-cut head. "You talk like you've already spoken to all of them."

"All last week. You should see my phone bill."

Murchison sighed. "I'm sorry, Otis. I agree in principle with what you're thinking. But the media would never let us get away with it. The NFL would be up to here in antitrust suits."

"I thought you'd say that," Otis said glumly. "If that's your answer, the game is ruined for this year. Take your Super Bowl trophy and put it with the others. But at the owners' meeting in Palm Springs next March you can expect a proposal for a rule change that no one over the age of fifty will be allowed to play in the NFL. For safety and insurance reasons, of course."

Murchison didn't say anything.

"It'll pass, Clint," Otis Pepper said. "It takes a vote of twenty-one out of twenty-eight to make a rule change. This one will pass twenty-seven to one."

Murchison said gently, "Old friend, I do, indeed, want to do only what is good for the game. Your vote would be 28–0. But it still won't work."

"Why not?"

"The new USFL. They'd snap Waller up so fast, he'd hardly have time to change uniforms."

"No, Clint, I don't think so. They may be stupid enough to play football in the summer with a bunch of cast-off players, but they aren't stupid enough to inherit the same problem that's breaking the NFL's back."

"You may be right, Otis."

"Well, I've taken enough of your at-home time, Clint. Be seein' you, and keep your peeper up."

"Otis," Clint said, "are you trying to say 'pecker'?"

Later that week Vic received a form letter announcing a reunion of his old Paschal High graduating class. There was a handwritten P.S. slanted across the bottom of the letter.

> Dear Paschal grad of '47:
>
> Most classes hold 25th reunions, but we somehow messed up and overlooked our 25th reunion. So we're having a 36th anniversary reunion on Saturday, May 28, 1983, at 6:30 P.M. in Ridglea Country Club, Fort Worth.
>
> Registration is $25 per couple, which includes dinner and dancing to Harvey Anderson's Orchestra,

which you will remember from the old days at the Casino and the Skyliner. There'll be a cash bar.

Make checks out to Paschal Reunion and mail to P.O. Box 1947 (how's that for getting a good P.O. box number?), Fort Worth, Tex., 76101.

Enclosed is a list of names from the '47 Annual, with check marks beside the names we can't locate. If you know of any of these addresses, please enclose them in your reply.

RICHARD PRICHARD
Senior Class President, '47

P.S.: Dear Vic,

Although the newspapers have stated you played football at Paschal, I'm afraid I don't remember you. But I certainly know of you NOW! Hope to see you at the reunion.

RICHARD PRICHARD

Dear Dick-Prick,

Enclosed is my check for $25. You may not remember me, but I was very close to Coach Abe Martin. He once wanted to buy me a rubber dolly.

VIC WALLER

....

14

On December 19 the Dallas Cowboys, who had already won their division and locked up the home-field advantage in the playoffs, drove a penultimate nail toward the unprecedented undefeated season by defeating the Eagles in Philadelphia, 22–7.

They did it, as always, on five field goals by Vic Waller.

A letter to the editor in the Los Angeles *Times* that week had a suggestion to offer:

"The balls that Vic Waller kicked on his record field goals were found and were sent to the Pro Football Hall of Fame.

"When they couldn't find the ball that Tony Dorsett carried on his record 99-yard touchdown run against Minnesota, the shoes that Dorsett wore that day were sent to the Pro Football Hall of Fame.

"So why not send Waller's right kicking shoe to the Hall of Fame?

"With his right leg in it."

Vic and Ellen became an "item," first in the local columns and then in the national ones.

Liz Smith wrote in the New York *Daily News* that "the beautiful Ellen is 25 years younger than the widowed

Waller, and no fan of football. It wouldn't bother her a bit if the Cowboys lost early in the playoffs so they could get on with the wedding. But with the way Vic has been kicking all those miraculous field goals this year, it looks like the honeymoon will have to wait until after the Super Bowl."

One of the supermarket tabloids headlined WILL OLD AGE CREEP UP ON KICKER'S BRIDE?

Because it was Ellen's first marriage, they decided on a church wedding. Ellen said she had always dreamed of being married in a little dollhouse church on Lackland Road in Fort Worth that was straight out of a Norman Rockwell painting. But when she phoned the secretary at Christ the King Episcopal Church she was told that so many, many other brides wanted to be married in the quaint little church, the membership had long ago voted that only members of the church could be married there.

Undaunted, she sat down and put her writing skills to work in an eloquent letter to the church priest. The pivotal phrase in her letter was "I know it's not right to want to be married in a church just because of the building. But I have always felt that any building was secondary so long as God was there."

The priest wrote back that the church would be available to her.

"How does it feel," Vic asked, "to get your first nonrejection slip?"

BY PRESTON KINGSLEY
New York Times News Service

IRVING, Tex. (Dec. 26)—To the surprise of absolutely no one, the Dallas Cowboys Sunday defeated the New York Giants, 47–14, to end the regular NFL season undefeated at 16–0.

The team set a new NFL record, beating the Miami Dolphins' 14–0 record in 1972 when the league played only 14 regular season games. The Dolphins that year won their two playoff games and the Super Bowl, posting a record 17–0 season.

Undefeated teams, of course, don't play in next week's wild-card play-offs, but if the Cowboys should win their next two play-off games and then win the Super Bowl, they would finish at 19–0.

Although preseason exhibition games don't count in the official records, the Cowboys would unofficially be 23–0 for 1982, having won all four of their preseason games. In 1972, when the league played six exhibition games, the Dolphins won three and lost three.

The Cowboys won the finale in Texas Stadium Sunday against the helpless Giants on three touchdown passes by Danny White and touchdown runs of 10 and 42 yards by Tony Dorsett and Ron Springs.

But Vic Waller still kicked two field goals of 32 and 45 yards, ending the season with a record 189 points, which, unlike other kickers, were all accomplished without the addition of extra points.

By comparison, the Cowboys' kicker Rafael Septien set last year's league record with 121 points, which included 40 extra points. This year Septien kicked all of Dallas's extra points, without a miss.

Waller also never missed, his longest being a record 92 yards. His 63 field goals in a row bested by far the league record held by Miami's Garo Yepremian of 20 consecutive.

The Giants saw the handwriting on the scoreboard early, losing the opening kickoff on a fumble and then watching White drive the Cowboys . . .

On the last day of the year Paul Harvey devoted his national radio program to a dots-and-dashes review of 1982.

His most telling line came midway in the broadcast when he said:

"It was the year of *E.T.* in the movies, and 'O.T.' in pro football . . . (pause) . . . No, not 'overtime' . . . (chuckle) . . . but 'Olden Toe.' "

Both wire services named Vic Waller to their All-Pro Teams.

Both wire services named him the year's Most Valuable Player.

But, strangely, Vic Waller, the best kicker in the history of the National Football League, wasn't named to play in the post-season Pro Bowl in Hawaii. The players themselves voted on who would make the teams in both conferences. And Vic's peers in the NFC, even though they knew they could have a cinch at taking home the larger paycheck awarded to the winning team, apparently had decided they just didn't care about knowing the outcome of a meaningless game.

There were ten teams entering the three-week play-off race to the Super Bowl, three division champions and two wild-card teams in the NFC, and three division champions and two wild-card teams in the AFC.

The first week was the battle of the wild-card runners-up. The Cowboys, of course, had that week off, and Vic gloried in being able to sit at home that weekend and see *two* games. Ellen spent the time shopping for a wedding gown and making an invitation list.

In the AFC the wild-card New York Jets eliminated the wild-card San Diego Chargers in a close one. In the NFC the Washington Redskins, who might have been a division champ if they had been in any other division except the one dominated by the undefeated Cowboys, easily dispatched the wild-card Minnesota Vikings.

And then there were eight.

* * *

During the next week NFL Commissioner Pete Rozelle fielded a press-conference question that so far he had been able to dodge.

How did he feel, an inquisitor asked, about the fact that the Cowboys were still off the board?

"I feel nothing, one way or another," Rozelle said. "It is a matter of monumental inconsequence to me, and to the National Football League, what the gambling community of this country does. The National Football League never has—and never will—run its business for the pleasure or convenience of gamblers."

In Saturday and Sunday games Miami handily defeated Cincinnati in the AFC, and the Jets, surprisingly, eliminated the Raiders in the other AFC race.

In the NFC, Washington continued to advance, defeating Atlanta, and the Cowboys continued their inexorable roll, beating Green Bay on four Vic Waller field goals, 19–7.

And then there were four.

On championship Sunday, Dallas and their hated rival, the Washington Redskins, met for the third time in one season. Playing in Texas Stadium, in a title game that was blacked out in the Dallas/Fort Worth area because it wasn't sold out, the Cowboys won 26–17 on the four Waller field goals that Tom Landry knew were necessary to maintain the lead and ensure the win.

Over in the other league, Miami defeated the New York Jets.

And then there were two.

In two weeks it would be Dallas versus Miami at the Super Bowl in the Rose Bowl at Pasadena.

CHAPTER

....

15

Carl Castleman was a thief. But, like a constant drinker who doesn't consider himself an alcoholic because he always gets to work the next day, he never considered himself a criminal.

Criminals were people who robbed, killed, and raped. Carl Castleman was just a thief and a con man. "Anybody's money is my money, if I can get it," he would say. And Carl usually got it.

White-collar crime, he called it. Fake stock deals. Crooked poker games. Blackmail. Swindles. Pool hustling. Fleecing love-starved rich widows. Sometimes house burglaries, but only when he knew a family was away on vacation. And there had been a few times when he had rolled drunks for their wallets, but he didn't consider that robbery.

He never pimped, although there was a time when he hired a whore who would lie in a coffin at his house and rise up at the precise moment for guys who paid big money to get an orgasm that way.

And he never, never had any dealings in dope. Or rough stuff. Carl Castleman had never carried a gun, although he did carry a set of brass knuckles for protection from others he came in contact with on the shady side of the street.

Carl had never done an honest day's work since he dropped out of school and left home at the age of fifteen. He lived by his wits as a kid, and his extreme good looks as a man. At thirty-three, he was as blond and athletic as a pro golfer, and dressed accordingly. He was irresistible to women.

On a good year he figured he averaged $50,000. Carl always had a good year.

He bet sports compulsively, winning more than he ever lost, which was the only way he played any game. His credit was A-1 with bookies in Los Angeles.

And he was proud of the fact he had never been arrested, never fingerprinted, never even questioned by the police. There was no record on Carl Castleman.

He grew up in L.A., the product of a broken home in a seedy section of the inner city. He was beaten by a drinking mother and forgotten by an absent father he barely remembered. He started shoplifting at nine, stealing his lunch money at ten, getting girls in trouble at fourteen.

"You're no good!" his mother shouted at him as her slaps turned into punches.

Carl stood there and took the blows in his face.

"You're rotten!" she screamed.

He laughed at her, even as he felt the blood start to drip down his chin.

"You're . . . you're . . ." His mother was groping for words. Finally, she found one. "You're a little son-of-a-bitch," she snarled.

"You know best, Mother," Carl said.

He stole bottles of milk off front porches for breakfast and walked checks at lunch counters in downtown drugstores for lunch and supper. Every time he'd pass a blind man who stood daily shaking a cup of pencils on a street corner, he'd slap hard under the bottom of the cup and say, "Think fast."

He'd show up unannounced at the homes of friends and, uninvited, spend the night. He'd stay as many nights as he could before the parents told him he had to leave. When he ran out of friends, he lied about his age and joined the Army. When he tired of the Army, about the same time the Army was tiring of him, he produced his real birth certificate and was discharged.

Back on the streets of L.A., the word got around that Carl Castleman was a man who could be depended upon if you needed "something done."

His specialty was arson. Carl had a novel way of putting rival nightclubs out of business. He would soak a club with gasoline, turn on the gas jets, and then lower a light bulb into a box of kitchen matches. He was far away when the light became hot enough to ignite the matches. Sometimes the tables and chairs were blown two blocks away.

Between the ages of twenty and twenty-five Carl had been married and divorced three times. He thought he might have loved one of them.

On the Sunday night after the Dallas Cowboys and the Miami Dolphins won their championships, Carl Castleman came to the decision to put into operation a plan he had been thinking about for at least three weeks.

He contacted a bookie friend and told him he wanted to put down $25,000 on Miami to win the Super Bowl, if, of course, the odds were good enough. The pleased bookie told Carl he would give him 3-to-1 odds, which Carl said was good enough.

He then called two other bookies and made the same $25,000 bets at the same 3-to-1 odds.

The next morning Carl went to a theatrical shop and bought a brown wig and mustache.

And then he went to a pawn shop and bought his first gun.

CHAPTER

....

16

In the off-week before the Cowboys flew off for the week-
long Super Bowl hoopla in California, Vic and Ellen
signed the papers on their dream home in Fort Worth's
wooded Tanglewood development and booked a honeymoon cruise out of Miami to Nassau, St. Thomas, and San
Juan. The wedding, in the little Norman Rockwell church,
was set for the week after the Super Bowl.

The Cowboy organization, per tradition, invited wives
and girlfriends to go on the team charter flight that next
Monday to Los Angeles. Buses at LAX would transport
the huge contingent to the Anaheim Marriott, Cowboy
headquarters for the seven days.

Carl Castleman waited in the crowd at the American
Airlines terminal, unrecognizable in a nondescript business suit, close-cropped brown wig, medium-sized brown
mustache, and dark shades that completely hid his eyes.

As Vic and Ellen came through the gate, Castleman
quickly stepped through the crowd and began reaching
into his pocket as he strode toward them.

Vic saw him coming out of the corner of his eye. He
stood there frozen, half seeing the man's hand hurriedly
pulling something out of his pocket, his mind flashing
images of those assassinations. He knew he should do
something, but there was no time.

"Mr. Waller," Carl said, pulling out a leather case and displaying a police shield, "I'm Johnny Haskins of the LAPD. Would you and your lady please step over here with me?"

He led them to a secluded section of the waiting area and said, "I don't want you to be alarmed, but we've received a death threat on you. Nine times out of ten, these things don't mean anything, but my instructions are to take you to the Marriott in one of our unmarked vans."

Vic was puzzled. "What about my fiancée?" he asked.

"She's to go with the team, sir. We'll arrive well in advance of the team buses."

"Does the team know about this?" Vic asked.

"I don't know, sir, but my guess is that they don't. We just got the call an hour ago, while you folks were still in the air."

Carl looked around the terminal. "If you don't mind, Mr. Waller, we'd better do this right now, as quickly as possible, before the rest of the team deplanes. For all we know, the attempt could come right here. Right now."

He took Vic by the arm and turned him around toward the exit. Vic said to Ellen, "Honey, this is probably nothing. I'll meet you at the Marriott."

"All right," Ellen said nervously.

Carl walked Vic briskly out the door and took him to a blue windowless van at the curb. "In the back," Carl said, opening the rear door. "You've got no view in there, but we'll be at the Anaheim Marriott in thirty minutes. Get in, quick."

Vic scrambled in and Carl locked the door behind him.

Driving well under the speed limit, Carl laughed all the way to the furnished three-bedroom house he had rented under the name of Johnny Haskins the week before. The whole thing had been accomplished flawlessly in under three minutes.

The house, selected because it had an attached garage and one of the bedrooms had a private bath, was on a quiet street in south Los Angeles. Carl drove the van into the garage, pulled down and locked the garage door, and then unlocked the van's rear door.

When Vic looked up from his side-bench seat, he saw a gun in Carl Castleman's hand.

"The main thing is to know that I'm not going to shoot you, or even hurt you, unless you cause me to," Carl told his prisoner evenly.

Vic blinked at him and felt his stomach take a queasy turn. He said nothing as he stepped out of the van.

"Gee, this doesn't look like the Marriott, does it, Toto?" Carl smiled.

"Who are you?" Vic said.

"Like I told you, I'm Johnny Haskins, but I'm not a cop," Castleman said. "But I'm also not the guy who phoned the death threat. There is no death threat. You have absolutely nothing to fear as long as you do what I say."

"So what do you say, Johnny?"

"I say walk into the house, turn right, and go to that bedroom at the end of the hall."

Carl and his gun followed Vic into the bedroom. The room contained a bed, a chair, a dresser, a TV with a remote control clicker, and a transistor radio on the end table. He could see that the two windows in the room were nailed shut and covered from the outside with tinfoil wrapping.

A large chain, attached to the lavatory plumbing in the adjoining bathroom, and with an open ankle clamp on the other end, lay waiting on the bed.

"Sit on the bed," Carl ordered. Holding the gun in one hand, Carl leaned down and snapped the clamp around Vic's left ankle.

Carl stepped back and leveled the gun at Vic's chest. "Here's the deal," Carl said. "You're going to be here for a week, until after the Super Bowl. You'll be released—safely—at that time. I promise you, you won't be harmed, and will live as nice as I can make it.

"I won't bother telling you not to try to escape, because that will be impossible. The chain will allow you to move into the bathroom, of course, but no farther than this bed. There's a toothbrush, toothpaste, comb, and shaving stuff in the bathroom. You can take a shower by sliding your pants all the way down that chain, but you're stuck with the same clothes for a week.

"I've got a week's supply of frozen breakfasts, lunches, and dinners in the kitchen, plus a supply of gin, vermouth, and cartons of Kent cigarettes, which I read that you like. You've got TV and radio, but I'm not going to buy any newspapers, or anything else, for that matter, because somebody at the airport may have seen us and might have a description of that van, which, incidentally, doesn't exactly belong to me, you might say. I've got my own TV and radio and food in the other rooms, so you won't be seeing me but three times a day when I bring your meals in. If you need me for anything, just sing out for Johnny."

Vic said, "Which isn't your real name."

"Which isn't my real name," Castleman verified.

"Who hired you?" Vic asked.

"I obviously wouldn't tell you," Carl said, "but the fact is, I'm not working for anybody except myself."

"You expect ransom?"

"I said I was going to keep you until after the Super Bowl. I don't figure you're worth much ransom if I wait until after the game."

"Then why have you done this to me?" Vic asked.

"How much do the Cowboys pay you?" Carl asked.

"Thirty thousand," Vic said.

"You're in the wrong business," Carl said. "I'm going to get $225,000, and my season's just a week long."

Carl walked out of the bedroom, shutting the door behind him. He went to the phone, dialed the LAPD, and asked to speak to the chief of police.

A secretary said the chief wasn't in.

"That's all right," Carl said, taking a folded sheet of paper out of his pocket. "I have an urgent message for him, and I want you to write this down word for word."

"May I have your name, please?" the secretary said.

"No, you may not. Just be sure you're writing this down, because I'm only going to say it once."

After he had dictated the short and startling message, Castleman abruptly hung up the phone. He then called the city desk of the Los Angeles *Times*, dictated the same anonymous message, and hung up once more.

Then he went into the kitchen and fixed himself a double bourbon on the rocks.

Walking back down the hall with the glass in his hand, he opened the bedroom door and spoke to his shackled prisoner, still sitting numbly on the side of the bed.

"Hey, Vic, you hungry, or did you eat on the plane?"

17

The hastily arranged press conference at the Los Angeles Police Department was frantic, loud, and chaotic. The police chief read the telephoned message into a multitude of microphones held up to him:

"Victor Waller is being kept in comfortable isolation for the next week, and will be released unharmed in any way at the conclusion of the Super Bowl. There is no ransom demand. This is no kidnapping. This is merely to advise his friends, relatives, and loved ones that for the next seven days he will be out of circulation but well cared for."

The chief leaned forward into the microphones and cameras and said firmly, "The Los Angeles Police Department is not so naive as to be seduced by terms like 'comfortable isolation.' While it's true there has been no ransom demand for Mr. Waller, this is kidnapping, pure and simple, and it will be pursued in that vein, with every means at our disposal to track down the perpetrators of this criminal act."

A reporter shouted, "Has the FBI been called in?"

"We haven't called in the FBI, but that's automatic in any kidnapping."

"How many men do you have on the case?"

"Right now, the entire force has been alerted."

"Have you verified that Waller is really missing?"

"We have. Two men went to the Anaheim Marriott, where the Dallas Cowboys are staying, and learned from Mr. Waller's fiancée that Mr. Waller was approached at the airport this morning by a man posing as a policeman. The man said a threat had been received on Mr. Waller's life and that he had been instructed to personally escort Mr. Waller to the Marriott for his safety. This department has received no such death threat. The man was obviously not a member of the police force."

"What's the description of the suspect?"

"Mr. Waller's fiancée, Miss Ellen Wade of Dallas, described the man as a white male, about thirty, six feet tall, slender build, wearing a dark suit, brown hair, with a mustache. He wore dark sunglasses and she couldn't see his eyes."

"How did he identify himself?"

"Miss Wade said the man showed them a badge and said his name was Johnny Something. She can't remember what last name he used."

"Did he use any force on Waller?"

"No. Miss Wade said they were both so startled that they didn't have any reason to doubt the man was an officer."

"How is the fiancée taking all this?" yelled one reporter.

"She is distraught, to say the least."

"Chief, do you think Waller is being held here in Los Angeles?"

"We have no way of knowing."

"What do the Dallas Cowboys think about this?"

"They have made no official comment to us, but I'm sure you people will be contacting them yourselves."

"Chief, do you think the Miami Dolphins might be in back of this?"

"I'm surprised you would ask such a question," the chief snapped. "We have no suspects. Repeat, no suspects. And I think it would be highly damaging to irresponsibly bring the name of any team into this investigation."

But the Miami Dolphins were, indeed, brought into the investigation. A press conference not unlike the crowded one in the police department greeted Miami coach Don Shula at the Dolphins' hotel.

"The Miami Dolphins," he read from a prepared statement, "are dismayed at the recent news about the Dallas Cowboys. It was a shock and surprise to us, as it was to the entire nation. We have only hopes and prayers that Victor Waller will be released safely."

"Does that mean," one cynical reporter asked, "before the Super Bowl?"

"Of course," Shula said. "In the next five minutes would please me. We are talking about a man—about a person's safety—not about a football game."

"She is distraught, to say the least," the police chief had said.

Actually, Ellen had been panic-stricken ever since she had talked to the *real* police that day.

Then, as the story burst in over the newsroom wires, she found herself the object of constant interviews by the nation's major media.

Ellen Wade, accustomed to handling the press in her public relations job, was now bewildered to find herself the subject of news story interviews. She somehow maintained her composure until the last person had finally left her room at the Marriott. Then she collapsed in tears.

"Please, God, send him back to me," she cried aloud.

* * *

The minutes, the hours, the days, dragged by for Vic in his solitary bedroom.

All he could think about was Ellen. He cared not for his freedom, not for the Super Bowl. Just Ellen.

Tears had come to his eyes that first night when he had seen her interviewed on television. And he had watched every newscast since then, hoping to see her, hear her voice.

She broke his heart one night in an interview where she spoke directly into the camera to him.

"My Vic," she said haltingly. "If you are watching, I want you to know that I never leave our room at the Marriott. I want to be here because it's the only place you'll know to call once you are free. The players' wives are with me all the time. They've been so sweet. And, Vic, you're with me all the time too."

After three days there weren't any more stories on television. Vic assumed there were still stories in the newspapers, but he came to realize that on TV there's nothing so dead as yesterday's news when there are no new developments.

As he had been told, he saw Johnny only three times a day, at mealtimes, always heralded by a now-familiar figure in ever-present sunshades opening the door and saying "He-r-r-r-e's Johnny!"

Vic's days were filled with playing solitaire, which he unashamedly cheated at, and the blatts, bleats, and buzzers of daytime TV game shows. And when he was exposed for the first time in his life to the bittersweet miseries of daytime soapers, the romantic problems of the mythical characters only reminded him more of his love for Ellen. His nights were filled with visions of Ellen until sleep finally came, and he would awake the next morning with the immediate recollection of where he was and what had happened to him.

As promised, Johnny supplied Vic each night with

predinner martinis, which Vic drank more and more of to kill the long hours.

But as the days dwindled down toward Sunday, Vic became aware that Johnny was drinking far more than Vic was. He started coming into the room, clearly drunk, as early as the noon meal.

And without his gun.

THE SPORTS WORLD
OF BLACKIE SHERROD
Dallas Times Herald Columnist

ANAHEIM, Cal.—Back when ole Buster here was in knickers and wearing a leather aviator's helmet to school, the heroes were named Jack Armstrong, the All-American Boy, and Frank Merriwell, the All-American Everything.

Jack Armstrong, who feasted on Wheaties, was the top-dog athlete at Hudson High, but too often he was off hunting for the secret elephant burial ground with his girlfriend, Betty, and her boob brother, Billy, and Uncle Jim Fairfield, who was nearly as rich as Daddy Warbucks and only slightly less Republican.

But Frank Merriwell, who wore ice-cream britches, sleeveless letter sweaters, and straw sailor skimmers, was a College Man who excelled in *all* sports, every durn one of them, from sculling to boxing to baseball to track and, especially, football, which was played with a real pigskin in those days.

Unlike Jack Armstrong, who was unseen but imagined on radios that stood on four legs in the parlor, Merriwell took his dime-novel exploits into the moving pictures, where we could actually see him on Saturday matinees while munching Black Cows and Jaw Breakers and secretly lusting to be the next Frank Merriwell if we ever got to college.

Merriwell was so *good*, whether he was hurling a javelin or a real pigskin, that he was always getting

143

himself kidnapped by the baddies on the day before
the Big Game, most always with some team labeled
State on the wooden scoreboard.

There he'd be, trussed up in some abandoned
warehouse, until the fourth quarter, when a friendly
mouse would gnaw his bonds and he'd jump into
his conveniently parked Packard roadster and roar
off to the stadium Just In Time.

Quick cut to a wooden, open-air press box where
an announcer in a George Raft fedora spoke into a
pie-plate microphone. The announcer would say, "It
looks bad for Ivy, folks, with State still leading 6–0
and only two minutes to go. Wait a minute! What's
this? There's a youth in street clothes rushing up to
the Ivy bench. He's hurriedly talking to Coach Pop
Ivers and pulling on a jersey. I can't be sure, but
it looks like . . . Yes, yes, it is!"

Quick shot to the bench: "No time to talk now,"
Merriwell would tell the old coacher, usually Jack
Oakie. "Just let me in there."

And putting on his leather helmet, but neglecting
to change out of his ice-cream britches and jazzy
brown-and-white Oxfords, Frank Merriwell would
race onto the field, kneel in the huddle with his
jubilant teammates, and then proceed to run 80
yards through all the USC extras Central Casting
could muster for the tying touchdown. He kicked
the winning extra point, of course.

And we sat there in the dark on those Saturday
afternoons and bought it all, not realizing until
mature years later that no athlete was ever *that* good,
never got kidnapped before the Big Game, and *never*
escaped at the last minute to win the blamefool thing.

Until, by Gar, in the year of nineteen-hundred-
and-eighty-two, when we *did* meet a genuine Geritol
Merriwell, and he *was* that miraculously good, and,
by all that's sacred in the old dime novels, *did* get
himself kidnapped before the Big Game.

But will he show up before the fourth quarter?

Thursday afternoon, sitting the locker room of Ivy, which has since become known as America's Team, a young Latin named Rafael Septien, who was now going to get—to get back, if you will—his Big Chance in the Big Game, was startled to look up and see a familiar face walk into the room.

A face old enough to be his father. Could it be . . . ?

Rafael Septien said only five words.

"Uncle Ben!" Rafael exclaimed. "You came back!"

Crusty old Ben Agajanian, an Olden Toe long before the title was bestowed on the still-missing Victor Waller, had come home—summoned from neighboring Long Beach by Tom Landry to scrape the rust from a field-goal-kicking pupil who has spent an unproductive and ability-debilitating season kicking nothing more exciting than extra points.

It was an unexpected dream come true for Rafael Septien, who hugged Uncle Ben repeatedly and began prancing around the . . .

In Las Vegas, Kelso Chandler still got up every morning, had breakfast, kissed his wife good-bye, and went to the office.

He poured all his Super Bowl information into his mental and electronic computer and moved his fingers accordingly.

No home-field advantage for either team. No injuries for either team, but of course Vic Waller was "injured" and wouldn't play. Weather, no factor in California. The Cowboys had the better record, being the only undefeated team in the NFL. But the record had been accomplished with Vic Waller, who was no longer a factor. Miami had lost two regular-season games, not damaging except for the fact that one loss had been to a team the Cowboys had defeated. But, again, defeated with Vic Waller.

Click. Click. Click. Move. Click. Move back. Click. Move.

When it got to the point where Kelso Chandler wouldn't bet either side, he froze the number.

The Cowboys were back on the boards.

But Miami was favored by three and a half.

On the Saturday night before Super Bowl Sunday, Carl Castleman sat drunkenly in a living-room chair and reflected on the point spread.

"I don't care how many points they win by," he said aloud to the empty room. "I've got 'em at three-to-one."

18

It was ironic that Super Bowl XVII, in a season that had been immortalized for the field goal and then robbed of its all-time kicker, was won—and lost—on a field goal.

A sellout crowd of 103,667 crowded into the Rose Bowl on January 30, 1983, to see the favored Miami Dolphins take on the undefeated, but Waller-less, Cowboys in a game that would go down as the best, most exciting Super Bowl in NFL history.

And played before a TV audience of 40,480,000 households, with a 48.6 rating and 69 percent share—the largest in NFL history.

Pro football was back, because Vic Waller was gone.

The game had a spectacular ending, but no less spectacular than its beginning.

Miami won the toss and elected to receive. The Dolphins' Fulton Walker took the ball on his two-yard line, broke over the middle at about the twenty, and headed straight down the field, shooting past the last Cowboy, kicker Rafael Septien, at about the Cowboy forty. He raced into the end zone with a ninety-eight-yard touchdown, the longest kickoff return in Super Bowl history and the first for a touchdown. The extra point was good.

Up in the booth, where ABC was taking its turn at broadcasting a Super Bowl, Frank Gifford reeled off the stats record, Don Meredith narrated the replay, and Howard Cosell pitched in with an observation that no one had had time to think of yet.

"This is to take nothing away from Fulton Walker's truly fine run," Cosell began, "but do you gentlemen realize there might have been a reason for the breakdown in the Cowboys' special team coverage? This was the first time all season that the Cowboys have had to protect against a kickoff runback."

He let that sink in as Miami lined up to kick off.

The nightmare was just beginning for the Cowboys.

James Jones, the knee-injured Cowboy kickoff return man who had been waiting all season to run From Here to Eternity, took the short kickoff on his twenty and fumbled backwards as he was hit by three Dolphins. Four other Dolphins fell on the ball in the Cowboy end zone. Again, the extra point was good.

The Cowboys were down 14–0 without ever having run an offensive play.

For two people in the stadium it was a scene of agonizing *déjà vu*. Tom Landry, on the sidelines, was seeing a replay of what had happened to Dallas in the championship game against Green Bay for the right to go to the very first Super Bowl. Up in the booth, Don Meredith was also reliving that sun-splashed day from the 1966 season in the Cotton Bowl when he was quarterbacking the Cowboys.

"Oh my, oh me, oh my," Meredith groaned. "I've seen that scene before."

"January 1, 1967," Cosell chanted. "Only it didn't happen as quick to the Cowboys that day."

"Not in just two plays," Meredith agreed. "Green Bay received and it took Bart Starr a few plays to throw to Elijah Pitts for the opening touchdown. But then Mel Renfro fumbled the kickoff and somebody carried it in for another touchdown, without us ever running a play."

"That somebody who grabbed the ball was the aptly named Jim Grabowski," the encyclopedic Cosell said. "But, don't forget, Dandy Don, there was a Dallas quarterback named Meredith, Number 17, who marched the Cowboys right down the field for two consecutive touchdowns to tie the game 14–14 at the end of the first quarter."

"We still lost the game by a touchdown," Meredith recalled ruefully.

"Well, you can't say there isn't still plenty of time left in this game," said Gifford. "We haven't even hit the one-minute mark yet."

And Danny White did, indeed, drive the Cowboys straight to a score when Dallas finally got the ball.

But it was a Rafael Septien field goal they had to settle for, not a touchdown. And, as if they were yawning, Miami drove right back to match the field goal, and then, on their next possession, went seventy-five yards to kick a second field goal by Uwe von Schamann.

Cosell, who always did his homework, announced, "Have you noticed, gentlemen, that this game may yet be decided by a field-goal kicker from Fort Worth, Texas? Uwe von Schamann attended Fort Worth's Eastern Hills High School, a school which wasn't even built when Victor Francis Waller was going to Paschal High."

While Super Bowl–viewing parties went on in millions of homes across the nation, two people watched alone in solitary silence.

In a Los Angeles bedroom, Vic Waller sat on a bed with a chain attached to his left leg. In her room at the Anaheim Marriott, Ellen Wade sat in a chair feeling there was a chain through her heart, not even seeing the game unfolding before her, just hoping against hope for a news bulletin on the screen.

Miami's David Woodley, at twenty-four the youngest quarterback ever to start a Super Bowl, was having a super day, throwing for two touchdowns in the second quarter.

While Howard Cosell was saying, "This game is looking more and more like a blowout," Danny White was in a huddle looking at bloodied faces and saying, "If anybody feels like panicking, just take yourself out of the game. We can still win this thing."

Butch Johnson, repeating a phrase he continually mouthed every time he got into a huddle, said, "I got my man beat. I got that sucker *beat*! Call my number, man. Dial B for Butch!"

"Okay, Butch," said White, knowing that was somewhat close to the play Landry had just sent in. "Shut up and we'll do it."

The perfectly executed pass out of the shotgun caught the Miami safety out of position. Johnson shouted in elation as he crossed the goal line with a fifty-six-yard catch and immediately went into his California Quake dance in the end zone.

And then a strange thing happened to the elated Cowboys. Rafael Septien—somehow, someway—missed the extra point!

The score at halftime was Miami 34, Dallas 9.

"It's all but over now," Cosell said. "And I, for one, can't say I'm sorry to see the Cowboys losing this way. Parity has returned. *Football* has returned."

Carl Castleman clicked off his TV set in the living room, put on his dark shades, and lurched his way to Vic's bedroom, spilling part of his tenth drink of the day.

"Want company for the rest of the game?" he said to his prisoner, sitting on the side of the bed.

"Suit yourself," Vic said. "I don't have too much of a say in the decisions that are made around here."

Carl sat down heavily on the opposite side of the bed. "Aw, you sound like you're pissed off at me."

"What could possibly give you that idea?" Vic said.

Carl laughed. "That's all right, ole buddy. I know it's just because your team is gettin' the dogshit beat out of 'em."

Vic said nothing.

"Don't worry," Carl said, his words slurred. "Look at it this way. You still get your Super Bowl share, and you didn't even have to go to work today." He belched and shrugged. " 'Course, it won't be the winner's share, but payday is payday, I always say."

Vic stood up beside the bed to stretch. Carl stood up on the other side and walked over to mute the sound on the TV set. "Hate halftimes at the Super Bowl," he said unevenly. "I wanna see a variety show, I'll go see a variety show. I wanna see a football game, I'll go see a football game."

Vic looked at the silent, dancing images flickering behind his captor. Carl was swaying slightly, the glass unsteady in his hand. Vic couldn't tell, but he thought "Johnny's" eyes might be closed behind his sunshades.

"Gonna let you go, just like I promised, when this game is over," Carl said. "That is," he said, laughing, "unless you wanna stay for the locker-room interviews and all that shit." He took another drink from his glass and laughed again. "You just might. You're a weird little prick."

"How you going to work it?" Vic asked, edging ever so slightly toward Carl.

"Answer me first!" Carl snarled. "You wanna stay for the locker-room shit? When I ask a question, I expect an answer."

"No, no, I want to go just as soon as the game's over," Vic said lightly. He was now at the foot of the bed.

"That's better," Carl said. "Well, I'm goin' to work it the same way I did when we came in here. I'm goin' to put you in the back of the van, and take you out to a vacant spot that I got located, and let you off in a field, all safe and sound while I go on my merry way. You won't have any trouble. There's houses about a half mile away. You can tell them that ole Car . . . Johnny treated you real good."

He swung his head up suddenly, as if he had felt himself nodding away. "You'll say that, won't you? I've been good to you. I haven't hurt you."

"Sure, sure, I will, Johnny."

Carl lurched forward, a step closer to Vic. "Well, you damn sure better." Carl's head swayed back, and he shook it. He took another drink of the bourbon. "Not that I'd of ever had to hurt you. Nothin' to worry about with fifty-two-year-old farts. Guys get to be your age and they're just pussies."

"That's for sure," Vic said. "I never wanted any trouble."

"You gonna tell 'em I was good to you?"

"Yes. I said I would."

"Damn sure better."

"I will," Vic said.

Carl grinned. "Was it a pretty good plan? Did I pull this off pretty good, all by myself?"

"You sure did, Johnny."

"I thought of everything. Didn't leave a detail out. No way anybody can ever trace me. Thought of everything."

"Well, almost, Johnny."

His head jerked up. "Whaddaya mean?"

"You made one little mistake."

"What's that?"

"You chained the pussy's wrong leg."

For one horrified instant of awful realization, Carl Castleman's eyes opened wide behind his sunglasses. Then the right foot of fifty-two-year-old Victor Waller lashed out like a jet catapulted from a flight deck and crushed Carl's testicles.

Carl was lifted off his feet and hurled straight back into the TV set, as if he had been hit with a .45 slug. His sunglasses flew from his face, his wig fell over his forehead, his mustache tilted ludicrously over his mouth. He looked in dismay at his trousers, turning to a bright red, as his back slid down the silently moving dancers on the TV screen.

Carl looked up in bewilderment and disbelief at Vic, and made one helpless attempt to put his hand over his groin before he lost consciousness.

Vic quickly squatted down and went through Carl Castleman's sodden pockets until he found the leg-clamp key.

He sat back down on the bed to free himself, and then took the ankle clamp and snapped it shut around Carl's motionless ankle.

He walked unsteadily into the living room.

Vic picked up the phone, but realized he wouldn't be able to tell Ellen and the police where he was.

He went out the front door and looked in both directions down a strange street. On one corner he was elated to see a convenience store.

Vic began running down the sidewalk.

That's when he discovered that his right foot was broken.

CHAPTER

19

Luckily for Victor Waller, who was late to a football game, the Super Bowl halftime droned on like a baseball game that had gone into extra innings.

The pageantry was still going on when an ambulance and five police cars rolled up to the convenience store. The last squad car contained Ellen Wade, the first one Vic had phoned from the store.

She had answered on the first half-ring. "I'm free, baby, and I'm safe," he said.

Over her tears of elation, he said he would explain everything soon, but that she was to wait in the room for the police to pick her up and bring her to him. Then, and only then, did he call the LAPD.

They fell into each other's arms as soon as she stepped from the car, oblivious of the crowd attracted by all the sirens.

Then, and only then, did Vic and Ellen get in the back seat of the unmarked car carrying two detectives. Vic directed the caravan to the house a block away, saying, "I've got him chained in the back bedroom, but you'd better go in with your guns drawn. He has a gun, but I didn't find it when I went through his pockets."

The two detectives told Vic and Ellen to wait outside

until they checked out the bedroom. It took them only a moment to determine that it was, indeed, safe to enter.

They found Carl still lying on the bedroom floor, conscious now and moaning. The detectives handcuffed him, used Vic's key to remove the leg clamp, and fished out his wallet as the room began filling up with uniformed police.

"Says 'Carl Edward Castleman, Los Angeles,' " the detective with the wallet said. "That the name he gave you?"

"No," Vic said. "He said his name was Johnny Haskins."

"Look around out there for a gun," the other detective said to one of the uniformed officers. "Let's get this sweetheart to the ambulance. Jesus! Look at his pants!"

Carl was pulled painfully to his feet, looking dazedly at all the policemen around him. He shook his head, trying to clear it, as his eyes met Vic's.

"You . . . you . . . ruined me," he gasped to Vic.

"I guess football isn't the only kind of ball I can ruin," Vic replied.

As two uniformed officers hustled Carl out of the bedroom, one of the detectives took out his notepad and said to Vic, "Now, let's start at the beginning, Mr. Waller."

"No deal," Vic said. "My deal on the phone was that you were to take us to the Rose Bowl as fast as you can. I'll fill you in as we go."

"Well, I don't know—"

"That's right, sir," one of the uniformed officers said. "We're supposed to take him and the lady to the players' entrance in Pasadena. We can lead you with the siren."

Vic didn't wait for an answer. "Let's go, quick," he said. "Who's got an AM radio?"

"We do," the other detective said. "Been listening to the game all day."

Vic took Ellen's arm and led the way out of the house. He walked quickly, but tenderly, not wanting to limp.

* * *

The third quarter belonged to the Cowboys.

As the two police cars, sirens screaming, hurtled out the freeway toward Pasadena, Vic told his story from the back seat of the second car, trying to keep up with the game on the radio.

Everson Walls made one of his trademark interceptions and ran a Woodley pass back fifty-five yards for a touchdown. Septien's extra point was good.

Later, Danny White, passing on first down from his own twenty-five, hit tight end Billy Joe DuPree over the middle for what would normally have been a gain of ten or twelve yards. DuPree turned into a bull, ramming his way through linebackers and finally emerging in the clear at the Cowboy forty-five. He went all the way.

There was an uneasy moment as Septien's extra point again seemed to be doomed for failure. But it nicked the left upright and fell in.

And then, climaxing a long drive in which Tony Dorsett gained fifty yards on eight carries, Landry crossed up the Dolphins by sending reserve back Timmy Newsome into the middle for a four-yard touchdown.

Septien's kick made it Cowboys 30, Miami 34.

Not only had the underdog Cowboys scored three touchdowns in a row, the Cowboys' defense had completely shut down Miami's running and passing game.

There were still two minutes left in the third quarter when the two police cars slammed to a stop at the players' entrance and ordered a startled gateman to open up.

CHAPTER

20

Rafael Septien, who had missed an extra point on this incredible day, got his chance to bring the Cowboys to within one point of the Dolphins early in the fourth quarter.

Beginning from his own thirty, Danny White methodically mixed his short and long passes without an incompletion to carry the Cowboys to the Miami thirty. He still needed seven yards when he was forced to throw away his third-down pass.

"Field-goal team in," Tom Landry called out.

Ben Agajanian grabbed Septien's shoulder. "Just treat it like any other kick," he told the young kicker.

But as he ran on the field Septien thought to himself that it *wasn't* just any other kick—not in a Super Bowl!

As the world watched, Septien's kick carried to the left, a foot too wide.

The policeman approached Agajanian as Ben watched Septien coming off the field, already ripping his helmet off in humiliation. "Coach Agajanian," the officer shouted over the noise of the crowd, "you're to come with me to the locker room. It's extremely important."

Agajanian looked at the policeman in amazement. "Who says so?" he demanded.

"Vic Waller says so," the cop shouted. "He's in there changing into his uniform, but says he won't come on the field until he talks to you. He doesn't want anyone to know he's here until you go in there."

"You better not be kidding, man," Ben said.

And he took off in an old warrior's sprint, the younger policeman hard-pressed to keep up.

Ben burst through the locker-room door and looked at the knot of people standing in the small room that led to the closed dressing room. A uniformed cop, two guys in suits, a woman, and a Cowboy equipment man.

"In there, Ben," the broadly smiling equipment man said.

Ben went in and closed the door behind him. Victor Waller stood there, dressed in his uniform and holding his helmet.

Without a word, Agajanian went to Vic and embraced him. "I can't believe it, Victor. How'd you get away?"

"Long story, Ben."

"Are you all right?" Agajanian said, his voice starting to waver with emotion.

"Yeah, I'm all right. But, Ben, I got a busted foot. My right one."

Ben looked at Vic, not knowing quite what to say. "Lots of pain?"

"Pretty bad. But, Ben, I don't want anybody to know about it."

"You don't think you can kick with a busted foot, do you?"

"I *know* I can kick with a busted foot, Ben. But only once."

"Meaning . . . ?"

"Meaning, I've got one more kick left in me and I don't want Tom to put me in until it takes one kick to win or tie us into overtime. I've got no doubts about range, Ben. I just don't think I could do it twice."

"I *know* you couldn't do it twice. You kick with a broken foot and you're out of football forever."

"I know that, too, Ben. But I've already decided I'm out of football forever. I'm retiring after this game is over."

Vic reached over into his locker and lit a Kent.

"The team doctors would never allow it," Agajanian said, shaking his head and turning his back.

"The team doctors will never know about it, Ben. Tom won't know about it. Nobody knows about it except you and me."

"Then why did you tell me?" Ben asked.

"Had to," Vic said. "I can't have Tom sending me in for kickoffs or field goals that won't win. Just one kick, Ben."

Agajanian sighed and lowered his head. "I know how you feel, Vic."

"I *know* you know how I feel, Ben," Vic said gently.

Vic put his cigarette out and put his arm around Ben's shoulder. He said to the older man, "Besides, the way they're playing out there, they're not even going to need a field-goal kicker. While we two old farts have been fartin' around in here, they've probably already gone ahead of Miami."

"Let's go see," said Ben.

Up in the press box, Cowboy publicity director Doug Todd made the strangest announcement in his life over the press-box P.A. system.

"Some of you may already know this if your offices have called. The Associated Press has just issued a bulletin that Vic Waller has escaped his captor and is being driven here by the Los Angeles police. That's all the bulletin says, and the Cowboys can't add a thing to it. This is our first time to hear it."

The press box erupted. Thirty seconds later the crowd erupted as the same AP bulletin was announced over the field P.A. system. Almost at the same instant Frank Gifford was telling the world on television.

Then the stadium exploded as the 103,667 in the oval saw the police leading a Cowboy wearing a familiar 3 on his jersey, and holding tightly to the arm of a woman, to the Dallas bench.

The officials on the field signaled a time-out to stop a play that couldn't have been gotten off anyway. The Cowboys on the bench mobbed Vic Waller.

In the press box, Dan Jenkins, who considered himself too sophisticated ever to be affected by anything so incredibly dramatic, left his *Sports Illustrated* spot on press row and raced down to the Dallas *Times Herald* spot where Blackie Sherrod, his longtime friend and former boss, was taking in the sidelines mob scene through his binoculars.

"I surrender," Jenkins shouted. "Biggest story of all time."

Sherrod never removed the binoculars, savoring a moment of nonchalance.

"Frank Merriwell deal." He shrugged.

CHAPTER

························

21

But it was Miami, not the Cowboys, who had scored again as Vic and Agajanian had been talking in the locker room.

Von Schamann had kicked a thirty-yard field goal in the Dolphins' opening possession of the fourth quarter, making the score Miami 37, Dallas 30.

And the tough Miami defense began denying the Cowboys time after time in a bruising, bloody battle that would go down as the most furious and exciting in Super Bowl history.

Tom Landry was aware that Vic Waller was back on the sidelines and in uniform, but had been too busy to talk to him. And now Landry had no need to call upon his superstar. The Cowboys needed a touchdown to tie, and even two field goals wouldn't help.

Exactly five minutes remained in the game when the fumble occurred.

David Woodley was sacked by Randy White on the Miami forty-five and lost the ball. The Cowboys' John Dutton had it when the pile was unstacked.

"We're going for overtime" were the only words Danny White spoke in the huddle before calling the first play.

"Overtime, shit!" Tom Rafferty said through broken lips. "We're goin' for two scores!"

No one expected they'd get the first one on the first play.

It was a play-action fake to Dorsett off right tackle, with Danny White sprinting out to the left for a pass. Drew Pearson made one of *his* trademark catches in the end zone.

The Super Bowl crowd went wild as Septien's extra point went through. The Cowboys had come from being down 34–9 at halftime to a 37–37 tie in the game's closing minutes.

And there was still time for a field goal to win it. For either team.

Playing it safe, the Cowboys disdained an onside kick, and Septien kicked it into the end zone.

The Dolphins had it on their own twenty. A time-consuming drive, getting them into field-goal range, would give them the game.

"First downs, we need first downs," Woodley said in the huddle.

They got them for him.

The youthful quarterback passed and ran the Dolphins past the exhausted Cowboys right down to the Dallas fifteen. On second and ten, there were exactly nineteen seconds left in the Super Bowl.

Don Shula decided there was no sense in taking a chance on a fumble.

He sent von Schamann in for a chip-shot field goal.

A frenzied crowd and a nation of television viewers screamed in anticipation for what was obviously a sure thing.

Cowboys on the sideline threw helmets to the ground. "No way, no way he can miss!" Rafael Septien groaned to Vic and Agajanian.

"There is one way," Vic said, staring intently at the field where the Miami kicker was pacing off his steps.

"No way!" Septien shouted over the din.

"One way," Vic repeated.

The two weary teams took their stances. The ball was snapped and placed down. Von Schamann, head down, advanced and swung his foot.

BLOCKED!

A weary and battered Too Tall Jones, all six feet nine of him, had dug down deep for a last measure that was the only defense for a field goal that was too sure of a thing to be stopped any other way.

Vic leaped high, shouting in joy, seeing again in his mind that day at Thousand Oaks, a thousand years ago, when Too Tall had broken through and blocked Vic's first field-goal attempt against a rush.

But Jones wasn't finished. He followed straight through, his huge arms still uplifted, and *caught the bounding ball in full stride*.

He was lumbering toward the goal, roughly three hundred yards away, he figured, with no one even close to catching him, lurching, almost falling, in the unfamiliar role of a ballcarrier.

Once, he almost slowed to a stagger, until picking up speed again as a convoy of Cowboys began forming behind him.

He ran with the roar of the crowd in his ears, until he passed the thirty, until he passed the twenty, until . . .

Until he fell down.

He simply fell down on the ten-yard line. No one was around him. He apparently didn't trip himself. He wasn't out of gas. He just fell down.

Dolphins covered his prone form before he could even think of getting back up.

In the confusion, the official lost two seconds before stopping the clock. Three seconds remained in the game.

"Field-goal team in!" Tom Landry shouted over the noise. "WALLER! WALLER!" he shouted in Agajanian's direction.

Vic took two steps onto the field and then turned back to Septien.

"You want this one, Rafael?" he asked.

Septien put both hands on Vic's shoulders. "I thank you, Vic. But, no. I had my chance. You are the best. Go get it, Vic."

Vic looked over to Ellen, who had been trying to stay out of everyone's way.

"Go win this dip-shit game," she cried out.

Vic turned and trotted onto the field. The roar was deafening.

He marked the spot, took his steps back, and waited.

The Cowboy line dug in. Gary Hogeboom looked back for Vic's nod, and then turned to extend his arms.

Vic watched the ball spiral back, as he had so many times before. He saw it coming seemingly in slow motion, as he had so many times before.

He advanced and swung his foot. The pain was excruciating, and he heard the bone snapping like a rifle shot. He hopped backwards on his left foot until he finally fell down.

He watched the ball arching lazily, end over end, through the uprights twenty-eight yards away as the final gun went off.

He saw the scoreboard flash to Dallas 40, Miami 37.

The Rose Bowl was pandemonium.

And sitting there in the January dusk, knowing the world was watching, Victor Waller, fifty-two-year-old insurance man, savored his last hurrah.